Daughters of

A play

Don Taylor

Samuel French – London
New York – Toronto – Hollywood

DAUGHTERS OF VENICE

First performed on 16th July 1991 by Chiswick Youth Theatre, for whom it was written, at the Waterman's Arts Centre, Brentford, with the following cast:

Maestro Vandini	Adam Shapiro
The Madre	Lucy Taylor
Maestra Luciana	Juliet Ames-Lewis
Sister Teresa	Tassy Miller
Sister Annunciata	Jackie Chan
Maestra Anna-Maria	Natasha Daniels
Maestra Silvia	Erica Rossi
Maestra Candida	Georgia Murray
Maestra Lucietta	Becky Harvey
Soprana	Rachel Warriner
Anastazia	Emma Rios
Prudenza	Bianca Le Corre
Pellegrina	Anna Green
Paulina	Chloe Murray
Michelotta	Kate Clark
Margarita	Katryna Thomas-Shell
Fortunata	Charlotte Ashworth
Giulietta	Jenny Jermain
Chiaretta	Amber Gregory
Perduta	Daisy Guard/Lucy Flinders.
Figlie di Coro	Lily Allport, Sarah Jupe, Rachel Hillman, Eleanor Hodgeson, Gemma French, Martha Alker, Biddy Floyer, Natalie Hay
Don Antonio Vivaldi	Jonathan Taylor
Grimaldo	Dylan Dolan
Pazzo	Pete Ayres
Governor of the Ospedale	Lewis Albrow
The Contessa	Nicola Whitehead
The Young Man	Hannah De Lasti
Punch and Judy Man	Andrew Styles
Puppet Boy	Toby Gregory
Pedlar Girl	Fay Moodie
Tumblers	Anya Gould, Zara Stewart
Carnival Revellers, Nuns, Entertainers, Pick-pockets, Starving Children	Dinah Kenyon, Vanessa Cruickshank,

	Alex Rylance, Thomas Naylor, Julie Moore, Savi Singh, Tabitha Simmons, Johnny Harrison, Marcus Ames-Lewis, Elizabeth Richardson, Clare Reading, Joanna Ballentyne, Hattie Castleberg, Charlotte Hatherley, Meriel Spooner, Daisy Carrott, and members of the company
Milord	Jamie Woolgar
Bodger	Sam Cocking
Director	Barry Woolgar
Assistant Directors	Belle Conduct, Christopher Saul.
Designer	David Cockayne
Design Assistants	Lee Dawkins, Joanne Downs, Dominie Hooper, Katie Munday, Jackie Orton, Victoria Smith, Elaine Starks
Costume Designer	Valerie Spooner
Costume Assistants	Rosie Lumley, Jan Hillman, Judy Miller, Rosemary Saunders, Ellen Dryden
Lighting Designer	William Hastings
Movement	Andrew T James
Publicity	Tawny Gregory
Technicians	Naomi Hillman, Josh Pearcey, Ted Sherman, Mitch Latham, Richard Holmes, Ellen Taylor, Sarah McCormick, Sarah Kenyon, Andrew Taylor, Chris Sheehan, Elaine Finch, Andrew Forrer, Natasha Costa-Correa, Nick Seal, Omar Mossadeq, Charlie Young, Molly Young and the CYT Workshop

SYNOPSIS OF SCENES

ACT I   The vestry of the Church of the Ospedale de la Pietà, Venice.
          A December morning
          A street in Venice
          The Madre's room in the Pietà
          A street
          The Madre's room. Late evening
          Bedroom (Prudenza etc.)
          Bedroom (Candida etc.)
          Reception room of the convent
          An ante room

ACT II   The Madre's room
          A street. Morning
          The interior of the Pietà — Vivaldi's study, Silvia's room, the
          common room, Morning
          A square in Venice. Early evening
          The Madre's room. Early evening
          The square. Later at night
          The library. Night
          The interior of the Pietà. Night
          An ante room

Period — 1720

CHARACTERS

Of the Ospedale de la Pietà

Maestro Vandini
The Madre
Maestra Luciana
Sister Teresa
Sister Annunciata

Figlie di Coro

Maestra Anna-Maria
Maestra Silvia
Maestra Candida
Maestra Lucietta
Soprana
Anastazia
Prudenza
Pellegrina
Paulina
Michelotta
Margarita
Fortunata
Giulietta
Chiaretta
Perduta
Figlie di Coro (non speaking)

Of Venice

Don Antonio Vivaldi
Grimaldo
Pazzo
Governor of the Ospedale
The Contessa
The Young Man
Punch and Judy Man
Puppet Boy
Pedlar Girl
Tumbler
Carnival Revellers, Nuns, Entertainers, Pickpockets,
Starving Children (non speaking)

From England

Milord
Bodger

AUTHOR'S NOTE

Musical instruments in the early eighteenth century sounded, and in some cases looked, quite different from those in use today. For a producer — or prop maker — stringed instruments pose no problem. Although with their gut strings, different bowing techniques and lack of vibrato, they sound quite different from modern instruments — as countless 'authentic' recordings will verify — they look the same, or similar enough to pass on stage. Flutes, recorders, oboes, bassoons and clarinets — Vivaldi was one of the very first composers to use the latter — look and sound quite different, but non-practical prop versions can very easily be made from chair-legs or banisters by anyone with access to a lathe. There were no brass instruments, trumpets or horns in the Pietà orchestra. When Vivaldi wrote parts or solos for them, visiting musicians were employed.

Some instrumental props were made for the original production and they are available on hire from Chiswick Youth Theatre via Samuel French Ltd. A complete set of female costumes for all except the Carnival characters, designed and made for the original production, is also available for hire from Chiswick Youth Theatre, via Samuel French Ltd.

Other plays by Don Taylor, published by Samuel French Ltd

The Burston Drum (with Ellen Dryden)
The Exorcism
The Roses of Eyam
A Long March to Jerusalem

ACT I

Before the CURTAIN *rises we hear the first movement of Vivaldi's passionate violin concerto, "La Tempesta di Mare", Op. 8 No. 5*

As the first movement ends, the Lights go down. When they come up again, or the CURTAIN *rises, we hear the third movement beginning off-stage, and we see a representation of a back room, or vestry, behind the public area of the Church of the Ospedale de la Pietà, on the Riva del Schiavoni, in Venice, round about the year 1720. The concerto is being played in the main body of the Church, some distance away off stage*

In the vestry, there are lockers or places for about twenty musicians. By each locker there is an instrument case, and pieces of music, and all have dark warm cloaks, which incorporate large hoods, hanging by the lockers, in neat rows. The set is not detailed in a naturalistic way. The vestry is a bleak and practical place, but the set itself, behind this particular scene, conveys the richness, the enjoyment, the indulgence even, of Venice in winter, when Carnival is about to begin

As the third movement continues, a young girl, dressed in a plain white habit, which includes a rather attractive hood or cap, all soft lines rather than restrictive angles, comes in, carrying a large pile of music manuscripts. She is a small, bustling, energetic child of about twelve or thirteen, well able to stand up for herself. The music she is carrying is a set of orchestral parts, and she busies herself about the vestry, placing the correct parts in the correct places — which of course she knows by heart. Her name is Perduta

After a few moments Maestra Luciana enters, also wearing the same white habit as the small girl, though perhaps with a grey facing or collar, or some other indication of her status, and a more restrained hood. Maestra Luciana is perhaps thirty-eight or forty, but looks older. Her mouth is beginning to develop a downward pull at the corners, and she has a permanently troubled or suspicious air, that can easily develop into irritability. The small girl has her back to her, and Maestra Luciana watches her for a few seconds, disapprovingly

Luciana What are you doing? Why aren't you listening to the music?

Perduta Maestra Silvia told me to get the new concerto parts ready, Maestra Luciana, for the rehearsal.

Luciana (*moving across to look*) What concerto is that?

Perduta The new one for cello, Maestra Luciana, from Maestro Vivaldi.

Luciana (*looking at the score*) How can it be? He isn't in Venice at the moment.

Perduta No Maestra, it was sent from Mantua by special messenger, the parts only came this morning. The Cardinal especially wanted to hear a new concerto by the Reverend Don Antonio, and to hear Maestra Silvia play it.

Luciana (*drily*) Yes. His Eminence particularly loves Maestra Silvia's cello playing. Have you copied these?

Perduta No Maestra, the Maestro had the copies made himself, and will be sending his bill, the messenger said, by letter. I must begin copying another set tomorrow.

Luciana If you haven't begun copying them already. I don't trust you here while everybody else is in the church. Everything's for sale in Venice, and we all know how much some people will pay for a new concerto by Don Antonio. Who's paying you, eh? Who's bribing you for a set of parts from under your skirt?

She pulls at Perduta's skirts. Perduta moves away from her, and finishes giving out the parts

Perduta No-one's bribing me Maestra . . . Maestra Silvia commanded me to come here during the last concerto to get the parts ready, because there isn't much time today. And everybody else isn't in church, Maestra.

Luciana What? What do you mean?

Perduta (*slightly cheeky*) You are here, Maestra.

Maestra Luciana looks at her sharply, and Perduta makes sure she is out of range before she continues quickly

You can't punish me Maestra, only Maestro di Coro Vandini can do that!

Luciana You are insolent. Only fit to scribble manuscript.

Perduta I don't just scribble manuscript, Maestra.

Luciana Don't answer me back! As if I care what you do. You are not an artist, you have none of the privileges of this establishment: you are not a true *Figlia di Coro*, only a hanger-on, a wretch dragged from the canal, only fit to soil your fingers with ink. Remember that.

Perduta Yes, Maestra.

Luciana I listened to Lucietta play her toccata. I have heard the storm-at-sea concerto so many times, I think I shall be seasick if I hear it again.

Perduta Did Lucietta play well, Maestra?

Luciana She played extremely well. She is my pupil, and I expect no less. There is no better young organist in Venice.

Perduta People say that she is just like you were, Maestra, when you were a girl.

Luciana I played better at her age. The word went round the city when I was playing. The church was overflowing, people stood out on the quay to hear me. But she is my best pupil in many years, I can say that. She is worthy of the Pietà. Is the new piece difficult?

Perduta Oh yes Maestra, very difficult. But not for Maestra Silvia. She can play anything. There isn't a composer in Italy who can write music she can't play.

Luciana (*looking at the music*) Well. She must make the most of it.

Perduta Maestra?

Luciana This is her last Carnival. She will be of age.

Perduta Oh. (*Wanly*) I didn't know that.

Luciana It's a microcosm of the whole of life here, child, being a girl of the Pietà. And none of us lives for ever.

Off stage the concerto comes to an end. There is a rustling of feet, the sound of the movement of many people, even restrained talk, but no applause

Perduta That's the end, they'll be coming in. It's sad there's no applause, isn't it. That's why I like it when we go out to play.

Luciana No-one asks for applause in a church. We play and sing for the Glory of God, not ourselves.

Suddenly the door opens at the back, and the whole orchestra streams in, looking just like professional musicians anywhere in the world after they have given a concert. The difference is, that these are all girls, all aged between ten and twenty, and all dressed in the same white habit and hood that Perduta is wearing. They come in talking, laughing, discussing what the concert was like, or more likely, what they will have for lunch, all moving to their positions, putting down their instruments, some of them even putting on their cloaks, feeling the cold of December in the unheated stone building. Some of them immediately see the new concerto parts and begin to look at them. For the majority perhaps it's just another pile of music, and at the moment they couldn't be less interested. Seven of the girls, the four Maestre, Anna-Maria, Silvia, Candida and Lucietta, and the up-and-coming Prudenza, Soprana and Anastazia, wear pomegranate flowers on their left temples, just above the ear, as a badge of their seniority

Prudenza, a lively fifteen-year-old carrying a violin, Pellegrina, a fourteen-year-old with an oboe, and Paulina, who carries both clarinet and flute, and is also fourteen, come on together and to to their positions. Like everyone else they carry a folder of music, which they put down. They are laughing and excited

Pellegrina Did you see him?

Prudenza In the same seat!

Pellegrina What!

Paulina Are you sure it was the same one?

Prudenza Of course I'm sure! I had a good look while Lucietta was playing her toccata!

They all giggle

Paulina I saw you looking.

Pellegrina So did Maestro Vandini, he was glaring at you.

Prudenza I edged a bit closer to the grille so that I could see right through. He was definitely there, sitting where he's been sitting at every concert for the last week. And so good-looking!

Pellegrina Did he see you?

Prudenza Of course not. No-one can ever see us, just our dresses.

Pellegrina No, you can be seen if you sit really close. (*Archly*) Someone told me.

Paulina Who?

Pellegrina Never mind.

The rest of the musicians have been entering and talking all through this section. Anastazia, a fifteen-year-old violinist, and Soprana, a seventeen-year-old cellist, are both looking at the new concerto. Next to them are a group of "initziate", young players slowly being introduced into the main orchestra, and thus becoming part of the Pietà élite. Margarita, violinist, is nearly thirteen, Giulietta, another violinist, is eleven, Michelotta, cellist, is twelve, Fortunata, oboe, is twelve, and Chiaretta, flute, only ten. They have only recently been introduced to the orchestra and are still overwhelmed and delighted, and full of hero worship for the senior girls

Anastazia What is it, a new concerto?

Soprana For tonight, apparently.

Anastazia begins to hum the ritornello from the score

Margarita Are *we* playing it? We don't have any parts.

Soprana No, of course not. *Initziate* never play when we go out.

Anastazia (*still humming*) Oh. That's a bit tricky . . .

Soprana What?

Anastazia All in unison though.

Margarita Sorry Anastazia. I forgot we were going out.

Giulietta You are silly, Margarita, you know that!

Fortunata Anyway, the parts would have been here.

Margarita Never mind. Wasn't Anna-Maria wonderful?

Chiaretta She always is.

Anna-Maria, who has just played the concerto, and Silvia, are just putting down their violin and cello. They are both twenty, fresh young girls still, but mature artists by now, and with something of the maturity that gives them as people

Anna-Maria Have you seen your part for tonight?

Silvia I've had a quick look at it.

Anna-Maria Difficult?

Silvia About the usual. He always makes the passage work as hard as he can, because he knows he can't catch me out. He's promised me one day he's going to write me a line I can't play.

Anna-Maria He never will.

Silvia As long as I have an hour to look at it . . .

Luciana is in a corner talking severely to Lucietta, who is not quite eighteen, rather young for her years and shy, not quite aware yet what an artist she has become

Lucietta I'm sorry, Maestra, I did my best.

Luciana I suffered with you, child, every note. You must do better, for my sake.

Lucietta I will, Maestra, I promise you. I thought it was going well.

Luciana It was not, child. The semi-quavers over the staccato bass were grotesque . . .

Maestro di Coro Vandini comes into the room and makes straight for Anna-Maria and Silvia. He is the current director of the orchestra and choir, Vivaldi having been on his travels for several years. He is perhaps in his early forties, but seems older, with his grey wig and rather obviously rouged face

Vandini Brava Maestr'Anna, you played like an angel!

Silvia Like a sea-nymph you should say, Maestro, with all those waves. If she'd played like an angel she would have been drowned.

Both the girls giggle

Vandini But what a a ridiculous thing to say! You can't say "Brava, you played like a sea-nymph!" Whatever you were like, you were superb. Not even Don Antonio himself would have played it better.

Anna-Maria He would have played it a hundred times better. But I got all the notes in the right place.

Vandini Much more that that, much more! You liberated the soul of the music and let it speak.

The Madre di Coro arrives with Sister Teresa

Vandini sees them and turns to the Madre

Ah, Madre . . .

Anna-Maria I sometimes think he's going deaf.

Silvia What are you playing tonight?

Anna-Maria I don't know yet. I heard Albinoni may be there.

Silvia Likely. He's very friendly with the Cardinal, all that gang.

Anna-Maria So I'll probably have to play one of his. Otherwise "La Primavera," I suppose. That's what they usually ask for.

Silvia Well, it won't matter what you do. You can play the whole thing half a tone flat and he won't know. He won't even be listening. I, on the other hand, shall be gazed at all evening, playing or not. And go on my knees to be blessed by the Church at the end.

Anna-Maria His eminence loves the cello.

Silvia He loves my transparent muslin fichu more. You know Vandini has been told I must wear the habit I wore the last time. That's why. "Down on your knees child." (*She laughs rather harshly*)

Vandini has finished talking with the Madre di Coro, who is a nun of about fifty, with a somewhat stern manner which hides a motherly, even passionate nature. Vandini turns to the talkative girls

Vandini My dear children . . . daughters of the Muse . . .

He is making little enough progress, but when the Madre di Coro speaks the silence is almost instantaneous

Madre Silence please, *Figlie di Coro*! . . . Maestro Vandini.
Vandini Madre, your servant, as ever . . .

He bows, with slightly exaggerated courtesy, provoking some smiles among the Coro

Vandini My children, the programme for tonight's music at the Cardinal's palace will be Maestro Vivaldi's *Lauda Jerusalem*, the soprano solo being sung by Anna-Maria and the alto by Candida. Then Pellegrina will play Maestro Albinoni's *Concerto in D Minor* . . .
Pellegrina Oboe or violin, Maestro?
Vandini On this occasion, as the composer will be present, we will play it on the oboe . . . and we shall then sing my *Laudate Dominum* in G, the eight-part a capella version. There will probably be a pause at that point, while the Cardinal entertains his guests, and we will then play the eleventh concerto of Maestro Vivaldi's *L'Estro Armonico*.
Silvia The one with two violins and cello, Maestro?
Vandini Precisely, yes.
Silvia (*under her breath to Anna-Maria*) How did I guess?
Vandini With Anna-Maria, Prudenza and Silvia playing the solo parts. Then Paulina will sing my cantata *Ah Dio d'Amore!*
Paulina Soprano or tenor, Maestro?
Vandini The tenor version. The Cardinal always expresses himself amused at the spectacle of a girl singing tenor, though I have assured him it is quite a natural thing in girls, indeed, a great deal more so than his favourite and much pampered castrato, who without his disability, would hardly sing a note above G! . . .
Madre Maestro, shall we finish discussing our music?
Vandini Ah, yes, indeed, er . . . well then, we shall end the evening with the new cello concerto, which Maestra Silvia will play, and which we will rehearse in the Music Salon, immediately after Refectory. Now, as for the next two months . . . well, the Carnival is always a busy time — though indeed, it truly begins this evening for us, with the Cardinal's great assembly . . . however, we shall be giving three morning concerts a week, at twelve a.m. on Mondays, Wednesdays, and Fridays, as well as two sung Masses and the usual Sunday Offices. There will, I suppose, be at least two or three evening concerts, serenades, or private music parties, each week, and probably more than that. We are at the service of the nobility — and the rich — in this matter, as indeed, in all others. Perduta, you must have your fingers on every score we possess — and be prepared to work late into the night if we need new ones.

Perduta Yes, Maestro.

Vandini The Mass at this evening's service will be Marcello in E. Madre, is there anything you wish to say?

Madre (*crossing herself*) *In nomine patris et filii et spiritus sancti.* Amen.

All Amen. (*All crossing themselves*)

Madre The arrangements will be as usual when we play outside the convent or the church . . .

Vandini We shall probably begin about ten, after the Cardinal and his guests have dined.

Madre The Governors' Barge will be at the quay immediately opposite the church at about eight. We shall go in ordered procession from the Grille Gate, wearing our cloaks well wrapped around us — it is cold today, so that is a wise precaution — and our hoods well down, so that our faces will be hidden from casual passers-by. We will be playing in public, instead of behind our usual screen, so when we are not playing or singing, we must all keep our eyes modestly down, and not move from the positions allotted to us. If the time between the pieces is long, we must remain seated, with our eyes lowered, and not attempt to converse with the Cardinal's guests, or acknowledge them in any way at all. If asked to speak by a suitably high-ranking person, you must of course reply. If that person insists on removing any one of you from your seats, for conversation, or personal playing or singing in a private chamber, you must not refuse. Two nuns will accompany any member of the orchestra who is invited to converse with any of the Cardinal's guests, in the main chamber, or in private rooms.

Silvia (*under her breath to Anna-Maria*) Except me.

Madre Did anyone speak?

Silence. Madre continues

Tomorrow, the Carnival begins. No child of the convent is permitted to leave this building during the weeks of Carnival. Anyone who leaves without permission, will appear before the Governors, and will be expelled.

Vandini Well, er, that is . . . yes. We must be most strict in this matter. However . . . ? (*He looks towards Madre for confirmation of his lenience towards all good musicians, which does not come*)

Madre The only exceptions to the rule will be for the whole orchestra or choir performing in the city, or for those members of the *Privilegiate* whose private teaching cannot be conducted within the convent walls. Let me remind you all that the Carnival is a time of the greatest possible temptation. Some might say that is its purpose — and see the hand of God in it. As children of the Pietà, even as the privileged *Figlie di Coro* we must ensure that not only do we resist all such temptation, but that we conduct ourselves in such a way that it has no opportunity to come near us at all. (*Crossing herself again*) *In nomine patris filii et spiritus sancti.* Amen.

All Amen.

Madre You may go to the Refectory now.

The girls begin to break up and to talk quietly

Do not leave your instruments or your cloaks behind you. Perduta will collect all your music, except the new concerto, which you should take with you.

The whole group is streaming off-stage into the main convent building

We hear Prudenza and Pellegrina exchange a few words downstage

Prudenza I'm going out to the Carnival this year. Are you coming with me?
Pellegrina How can we?
Prudenza I'm going to find that beautiful young man.
Pellegrina Prudenza, you don't dare!
Prudenza I do. But do you?

They both go off together, giggling excitedly

The Madre makes her voice heard again

Madre I wish to speak to Anna–Maria, Silvia and Candida for a few moments on their own. So the rest of you go as quickly and quietly as you can . . . Perduta.
Perduta Yes, Madre?
Madre Leave us now. You can collect the music in a moment.
Perduta Oh, but Madre ——
Madre Do as you are told, child!
Perduta Yes, Madre.

She scurries off with the rest. The stage rapidly empties

The Madre stays with Sister Teresa and the three senior girls, who have some idea what is coming, and throw apprehensive looks at each other. When all the members of the Coro have gone, the Madre begins, formally at first, but rapidly becoming more personal

Madre My children . . . you are three of the brightest stars in the firmament of the Pietà. Visitors from Paris and Dresden ask where they can hear Anna-Maria and Silvia, and Candida is not far behind them in her fame. God has poured his gifts liberally upon all three of you, and living here has allowed you to develop them as fully as you can. But, there comes a time for all the children of this convent — the saddest time, for us, who live here all our lives — when we must say goodbye. The Governors decree that no child shall stay here and receive the support of the State of Venice beyond the age of twenty years. I don't need to remind you of what this most Serene Republic has done for you. You are all orphans, or have lost sight of your parents, and have spent almost all your lives here. Without the liberality and care of this convent, it is unlikely you would have lived to be ten, or even five. So when the Carnival is over, we must, reluctantly, open the doors of this establishment, and shut them again, with you on the outside. You have realized that, I hope, all three of you.

All three Yes, Madre.

Madre There are only three realistic choices open to you. The best is that you should profess yourselves as nuns and become sisters of this order. The next best is that you should marry well enough to survive in the kind of life you have become used to. The third choice, that you should become a teacher here, and pass on your skill to your younger selves, is not at this time open to you. We have all the teachers we need. There is a fourth option — I cannot call it a choice — which leads to degradation and probably death. There is no way a woman can survive on her own in Venice. Do not imagine there is. (*She pauses for a moment*) Except the one too shameful to name, which gives this city so many homeless children to care for. The lawful marriage bed, or a spiritual marriage to Christ, are the only real choices you have. Do you understand that?

All three Yes, Madre.

Madre After the Carnival is over, you will be summoned before the Governors of the Pietà, who are all noblemen from the families of the Golden Book of Venice, and they will tell you when you must leave. At that point you will be assisted into a suitable convent, if that should be your choice. But ——

She nods to Sister Teresa, who leaves, closing the door behind her, but remains visible beyond it as she stands on the other side of the grille. When they are alone the Madre speaks carefully, aware she is breaking the rules

—the point of my talking to you here, when all the others have gone, is to speak privately to you, as though I were your real mother, rather than your mother in Christ . . . (*There is some feeling, even emotion in her speech*) Do not misunderstand me, when I say . . . that these next two months of Carnival are your opportunity. If you wish to marry — and we shall not allow you to marry less than well — this is your best chance. You will spend a good deal of time playing and singing in public, where you will be seen as well as heard. You are all three great masters of your art, and for that alone, apart from your personal qualities, you will be much admired. Be modest, be worthy children of the Pietà, do not, in any sense, sell yourselves. But remember what I have said to you; and think of it as good advice, from a woman who has played this scene too many times to enjoy it. It is always the saddest part of our life here, but it is a necessary part. Because, if you did not go, how could we continue to help the abandoned and orphaned children of Venice as we do? If . . . you are approached by gentleman of merit and rank, you will be allowed to meet, chaperoned, of course, by two masked sisters, who will always be different, so that there will be no possibility of bribery. Do not repeat what I have said to you. It is advice given by a friend, rather than the Reverend Madre di Coro. And do not fear to come to me in confidence, if you need further advice, or if there is anything I can do to help you. Have you anything you wish to say?

Silence

Or to ask me?

All three No, Madre.
Madre *In nomine patris et filii et spiritus sancti, Amen.*
All three Amen.

The Madre pauses for a brief second, then goes out without speaking, Sister Teresa opening the door for her the moment she moves, by unspoken command

For a moment the three girls look off after her, then at each other

Silvia Well . . !

A pause

Anna-Maria Have you thought about it?
Candida I've been thinking about it for a year. Haven't you?
Anna-Maria No, not really. There hasn't been time.
Silvia The old bawd!
Candida What?
Silvia All that "Don't be afraid to come to me for advice. But do keep it a secret!" She's an old witch. They all are.
Anna-Maria What do you mean?
Silvia She was giving us a private message, in a respectable code, so she doesn't have to spell it out.
Anna-Maria I don't understand.
Silvia She will fix us up! That's what all that roundabout piety was leading up to! She knows there are hundreds of men in Venice who can't wait to get their hands on a pure little girl from the Pietà, and she knows how much they will pay for the privilege! She won't force us. But she can "help". And she'll get a large fat purse full of ducats as her part of the bargain!
Candida Is that true?
Silvia "Don't sell yourselves," she said. She means let me do the selling for you!
Anna-Maria No. I don't think so.
Candida You're too cynical, Silvia.
Silvia I have good reason to be.
Candida What are you going to do?
Silvia Not shut myself up in a nunnery for the rest of my life, that's for sure. What about you, Anna?
Anna-Maria I just want to keep on playing. I don't care how. I've been playing ever since I can remember, and I can't imagine what life would be like without it.
Silvia I can. Easily. I can think of better things to put between my legs than a cello.
Candida Silvia!
Silvia You'd better bind up your ears tonight at the Cardinal's. You'll hear a lot worse than that!
Anna-Maria What will you do?
Candida I don't know. I was brought here as a baby. I've never known any other life. It frightens me to think of outside.
Silvia That's because you've not been out enough. It's wonderful out there.

That's where life is, not in here. I can't wait.

Anna-Maria I can't imagine not playing the violin. But you can't in a convent. Or when you're married.

Silvia Marry the right man and you can. In the meantime, I have to play this tiresome string of notes the Maestro has constructed for me.

Anna-Maria But you love playing.

Silvia Of course I do. I like anything I do well.

Perduta enters tentatively

Perduta Can I come in, Maestra Silvia? I have to collect up the music.

Silvia Yes, of course you can.

Anna-Maria We'll leave you alone. To study your concerto.

Silvia Well, I suppose I had better glance through it. Just to make sure he hasn't put in something to trick me.

Candida You're too arrogant, Silvia.

Silvia And you, Candida, are not arrogant enough.

Candida No. That's true.

Anna-Maria We'll see you at rehearsal.

Silvia If I bother to come!

Anna–Maria and Candida go out

Silvia is audibly humming through her part, just under her breath as Perduta collects the music

Perduta (*tentatively*) Is it true you have to leave soon, Maestra Silvia?

Silvia Yes. It is.

Perduta Won't you be very sad?

Silvia Of course I shall be. I have been here since I was four. I've made some good friends.

Perduta I came as a new-born baby. I was left at the grille with a note.

Silvia Did it say who you were?

Perduta No. Just "Pray for me and save my child."

Silvia Touching.

Perduta So I might be a princess.

Silvia Or a whore's brat.

Perduta I shall be very sad to see you go, Maestra Silvia.

Silvia I have the faintest recollection of another life. I don't know what it was, except that it wasn't poor. I can remember lights, and rich colours, clothes, music. I think I can. And my mother, with large dark eyes, and hair like a jet black fountain, falling all over me.

Perduta Perhaps *you* are a princess then?

Silvia A whore's brat just as likely. A better class of whore though.

Perduta Aren't you sorry to be going?

Silvia No. I'm not.

Perduta I wish I could go with you.

Silvia Good God! What would I do with you? I shan't want a copyist where I'm going.

Perduta Where's that?

Silvia Never you mind, little girl left at the grille. Have you finished?
Perduta Yes, Maestra Silvia, I have.
Silvia Then go. I haven't read this through yet.
Perduta Yes, Maestra.

Perduta goes. Silvia follows her off, holding the score, and humming to herself

The scene changes to a street in Venice. Several alleyways lead on to a small square

Milord enters. He is an Englishman in his middle twenties, blank, good-looking, good-hearted, and immensely stupid beneath his fashionable charm. He comes out of one alley, and looks into another, then comes DS and calls

Milord Bodger!

Milord then exits up another alley just as . . .

Bodger enters from the alley Milord has not looked down

This is repeated as many times as the director or the audience can stand, until at last Milord and Bodger manage to come on stage at the same time. Bodger is a servant of about twenty, open-faced, energetic, keen, always helpful, but not overburdened with brains, a fact which he makes up for with a liberal amount of low servant cunning

Bodger Yes, sir?
Milord Where are you?
Bodger Here I am, sir.
Milord Whenever I look for you, you're not there.
Bodger I am now, sir.
Milord What?
Bodger There. I mean here.
Milord For a gentleman's man you leave a lot to be desired.
Bodger Surely not, sir?
Milord Yes, you do.
Bodger I didn't know you desired gentlemen's men that much, sir.
Milord Bodger, you're a good-hearted fellow, but you're useless. What are you?
Bodger A good-hearted fellow, sir.
Milord What do you think of Venice?
Bodger Fine, if you like water.
Milord Isn't it splendid?
Bodger And you don't mind getting your feet wet in the main road.
Milord Magnificent?
Bodger And you don't drive coaches for a living. Good place for getting drowned though. I don't like all these alleys.
Milord What's wrong with them?
Bodger Too narrow. Too dark. Too full of Italians.
Milord Bodger, you are an Englishman and a Philistine. You have no love

for art, and your natural reaction to anything foreign is to say if it was any good we'd have it in England.

Bodger Yes, sir. That makes sense.

Milord But let me tell you, there is no city in the world like this one! When I came here on the Grand Tour, to finish off my education ——

Bodger Did you finish it off, sir?

Milord Completely!

Bodger Oh good.

Milord I have never experienced a time of such sustained delight: and I've never experienced it since.

Bodger Oh, I am sorry to hear that, sir.

Milord And now that I have come so unexpectedly into my inheritance, I couldn't wait to come back! Bodger, we have so much money, we can hardly put one leg in front of the other with the weight of it!

Bodger Really, sir? I hadn't noticed.

Milord I was speaking metaphorically.

Bodger Oh well, you can't expect me to understand then. I don't speak metaphoric.

Milord We are loaded, Bodger!

Bodger So what are you going to do, sir, with all this cash?

Milord Do you know what I remember most, Bodger, from my last trip?

Bodger No sir. But I shouldn't think it's the sort of thing you can say in public.

Milord I was here with a man who knew Venice well, and he took me down a certain street — how shall I describe it? At every doorway and window there were men and women with the most inviting looks on their faces. And they all kept coming out towards my friend, jabbering in Italian — which I didn't speak then — and pointing to me, and smiling!

Bodger Laughing, even . . .

Milord I asked my companion, what were these people selling. And he turned to me and said, "My friend, whatever you want, they're selling it!"

Bodger He didn't!

Milord I tell you he did!

Bodger What did you buy?

Milord Never you mind.

Bodger Can I buy some?

Milord Bodger, I have never forgotten that moment, and now that I own most of Leicestershire, I have come back, to claim my Italian inheritance!

Bodger What are you going to buy, sir? You can tell me, I won't let on to a soul.

Milord We are going to buy paintings, Bodger, and music!

Bodger You're not serious!

Milord And wine, and pleasure, and all the glory of life!

Bodger Now you're talking, sir, that sounds more like it!

Milord Most of all Bodger, we are going to buy a delightful, charming, sloe-haired, plum-eyed, peach-skinned, cherry-lipped, sensual Venetian beauty!

Bodger And then we'll eat her with cream.

Milord The women here, Bodger, are like no other women on earth! I have never forgotten the women I met here! We shall buy the most charming girl in Venice, and take her back to England with us!

Bodger But what will Madam your wife say?

Milord She won't say anything Bodger, because she won't know! She is my duty as a gentleman. But my little Venetian beauty will be my pleasure as a scoundrel!

They both roar with laughter

Bodger Perhaps she won't want to be bought, sir? Most women I know don't.

Milord In this city, Bodger, you can buy anything, if you have enough money. And I do! And of course, I won't *tell* her I've bought her. I shall woo her with all the charm I possess!

Bodger Oh, that'll be all right then.

Milord And set her up in Venetian splendour in the West Wing. My wife can't stand the West Wing, she never goes there: it's too long a walk. And there I shall have a Venetian mistress, all of my own!

Bodger Sounds fine, sir. So long as the girl will put up with it.

Milord What do you mean, put up with it? What greater honour could any foreign woman aspire to than to be an Englishman's mistress? It's the crowning glory of her sex!

Bodger Well, sir, it sounds like we're going to have a very good holiday.

Milord Carnival begins tomorrow, and we must get masks and cloaks and three-cornered hats, and prepare to enjoy ourselves, incognito.

Bodger Does that mean legally or illegally, sir?

Milord It means Bodger, there's no difference! There is you, and there is this unknown beauty. You don't know who she is, and she doesn't know who you are, and neither of you cares!

Bodger I say that every time, but they always say no.

Milord Not here they don't! The first thing, Bodger, is to get us in to the Cardinal's great assembly tonight, in his palace on the Grand Canal.

Bodger How do I do that, sir?

Milord With money, Bodger, with money! What other way is there?

Bodger None that I know, sir. Where is the Grand Canal?

Milord Just keep walking that way and you can't miss it!

Bodger After you then, sir. I haven't been to a good Cardinal's party in years . . .

They both go off

The scene changes to the Madre's room in the Pietà — a sort of office or administrative centre. A table, chairs, a large hung crucifix and many ledgers, containing hundreds of years of information

The Madre enters, followed by Maestra Luciana. As the door opens we can hear the sound of all kinds of instrumental and vocal practice and rehearsal, which becomes inaudible when the door is closed

Luciana I must have more teaching time! At the moment I have only eight hours a week. Some days I have no time at all!

Madre I'm sorry, Maestra, that is the only time allocated.

Luciana I need eight hours a week with Lucietta alone, if she is to fulfil her promise . . .

Madre Lucietta is already a great master, her name is being spoken all over Venice. I can hardly see she needs to do any more than play and deepen her private study.

Luciana That, Madre, is because you are not a musician, and I am! And what am I to do about the younger pupils, with so little opportunity to teach them?

Madre There are only four of them, Maestra, and they all play at least two other instruments, as well as singing in the choir . .

Luciana Exactly! I need far more pupils, I could teach twice as many, three times. Why am I spending half the week doing nothing?

Madre Well, Maestra . . .

Luciana Can't you get me another half a dozen girls from among the Commoners? They must have some music in them somewhere, and I can do the rest.

Madre The Governors are very strict, Maestra, in the matter of numbers. We can't go and seize a handful of Commoners just when we feel like it.

The door opens, and one of the Governors enters. He is a Venetian nobleman of about forty, with the mind and manner of an accountant

Governor Reverend Madre di Coro, excuse my interruption, and you, Maestra Luciana . . .

The two women both curtsy

Madre Not at all, signore, we are always at the Governor's disposal.

Luciana (*smiling winningly, kissing his sleeve.*) Signore . . .

Governor Maestra Luciana, it is always a pleasure to see you. I thought Lucietta played quite brilliantly yesterday. She is an ornament to the Pietà!

Luciana Thank you, signore. I have taught her with particular care.

Governor All you know, I daresay.

Luciana Some of what I know, certainly. (*Luciana blushes with pleasure*)

Governor I speak for the Council of Governors, not for myself. For the two months of Carnival I have been deputed to act on their behalf.

Madre We are glad to welcome you to the task, signore.

Governor Well, we must all take our turn, and it is a particular delight that mine falls during Carnival. However, I have to tell you that my visit is not altogether a pleasant one.

Madre I'm sorry to hear that . . .

Governor The Governors are becoming most concerned about the state of the Pietà's finances. Prices, as we all know, continue to rise, and so do costs. There are a thousand girls here, under the Pietà's care ——

Madre Nine hundred and thirty-eight to be precise, sir.

Governor — of which only fifty are *Figlie di Coro*. The concerts we give in the church bring in a substantial return, but, as you are well aware, nothing like enough to run an establishment on this scale. And the State of Venice runs three others of a similar size. Of course, the work we do here in saving the abandoned and starving children of the city is of the greatest value, but — to put it bluntly — it costs too much: the subsidy required is too high, and it is getting higher by the year.

Madre I don't see what else we can do sir, we ——

Governor Excuse me, Madre . . . We intend to have the closest look at the whole running of the Ospedale, to see where savings can be made. We shall make substantial cuts, you may be sure.

Madre But what can we do, sir? If we turn children away they will starve in the steets, or end up in the canal. Too many do that already.

Governor Of course, cutting the number of children will be the last resort. The very last resort. There are other measures we can take before we even consider it.

Madre What?

Governor There are many inefficiencies that have grown up over the years. Thousands of ducats can be saved.

Madre Well sir, I know the running of the house in detail, and I hardly think so.

Governor Madre. I know so . . . We must, in addition, find more ways, many more ways, of making money. We can charge more for the morning concerts. People will still come, they travel across the whole of Europe to hear the girls perform, and a few ducats more at the door won't stop them. We must also make it clear that private music parties ——

Madre We are a charitable community sir, a Godly foundation, not an Opera House! We cannot charge fees when we play!

Governor — that a substantial donation will be expected, and if it is not forthcoming, we won't play for them again. Then we can give more concerts.

Madre We sometimes play three times a day, sir, as it is.

Governor But not every day. And why not four times a day, if the public will stand it? Venice is always full of visitors, and they all want to see the orchestra play. They are strong, healthy creatures, your girls. They love playing.

Madre They will need to if they are to play four times every day.

Governor In addition, we must encourage the nobility and the rich to give us more: gifts, donations, wills, trusts, anything we can get our hands on. We cannot afford to turn away a penny, Madre, believe me. The situation is serious.

Luciana I'm sure I could stage more organ concerts, signore, if I were given more teaching time.

Governor Excellent, Maestra Luciana, that's exactly the spirit! Let me say

I don't come simply as the bearer of harsh news. Waiting in the ante room is a great Lady of Venice, newly arrived from Rome, who wishes to make a substantial donation to the Coro. I must ask you to receive her with the greatest courtesy, and to make sure that she gives us the maximum possible amount. Everything in the future is going to depend upon such people. The old days, of bottomless subsidy from the Venetian State, are, I'm afraid, over.

Madre Of course I'll see her at once, don't keep her waiting in the ante room like a postboy or a tradesman . . .

The Governor looks off stage

Governor Madam, my lady . . . if you would be so condescending as to walk in . . . (*He ushers her in bowing and scraping almost to excess*)

The Contessa enters

Her Serene Highness, the Contessa di Montefalcone! We are all most obsequiously at your service, my lady.

Contessa Good-morning, Reverend Sister, Maestra.

Luciana Good-morning, my lady.

The Contessa is a magnificent sight, like a galleon in full sail, a great lady of eighteenth-century Venice, with both the extravagance and the taste of that great city, and its coolness and natural acceptance of its extraordinariness. She is, to begin with, a very beautiful woman, in the very prime of life, probably somewhere in her late thirties. She wears a hooded cloak, which she removes later in the scene, revealing the full glories of her restrained but amazing day dress. There is enough black in her outfit tastefully to hint at the widow, not enough to tarnish the splendour of her appearance

Madre The blessing of God on you, my lady, in this Holy Place.

Contessa May it be on all of us.

Governor The Contessa has just returned to Venice after many years' residence in Rome and Naples. She has particularly fond memories of the music at the Pietà.

Contessa My husband, the Count, was a great connoisseur of music. He died last year, in Rome ——

Madre Peace be to his soul, may he find eternal rest, Amen.

All Amen.

Contessa —— and left me extremely well provided for. I have decided to return to Venice, for part of the year, at least, and I have bought a palace on the Grand Canal. A delightful place, small, but charming. Like any religious widow, I would like to make a substantial donation to the Pietà.

Governor Thank you, my lady.

Contessa You are responsible for the day to day running of the Coro I believe, Madre?

Madre And the girls' welfare, my lady.

Contessa Then I must speak to you. Alone, if you please sir, Maestra.

Governor (*bowing out*) Of course, my lady, of course. I shall attend you in
the ante room.
Luciana My lady . . .
Contessa Yes, yes, of course . . .

The Governor and Luciana exit

*The Contessa hurries them out very briskly, and shuts the door herself. Then
she looks round at the Madre and walks around the room a little. The Madre
is waiting for her to speak, but she seems not quite sure how to begin*

Madre Please be seated, my lady.
Contessa No, I'll stand for a moment . . .
Madre Can I get you anything? A cordial?
Contessa No, nothing . . . How old are you?
Madre I beg your pardon, my lady?
Contessa You heard me. How old are you?
Madre I'm nearer fifty than forty, my lady . .
Contessa Tell me the truth!
Madre I am forty-nine, my lady.
Contessa And what is your name?
Madre I am Sister Maria degli Angeli.
Contessa No, I mean your real name.
Madre I have no other name now, my lady.
Contessa The name you were born with, tell me!
Madre Maddalena, my lady.
Contessa High-born were you? Nobility?
Madre No, my lady, my father was a merchant.
Contessa Rich then?
Madre Not rich enough.
Contessa Is that why you became a nun? He couldn't afford to keep you?
Madre No. I had a vocation, from an early age.
Contessa How old were you when you took your vows?
Madre Twenty, my lady.
Contessa Late, if you had a vocation.
Madre I . . . it . . . it took time. It is a marriage, and marriage must be
undertaken seriously.
Contessa More seriously, I daresay, than most of the marriages I know.
So. You must be a woman of some considerable talent, to be in such a
position, and a poor man's daughter?
Madre We lay all our talents at the feet of Christ, my lady.
Contessa Yes. . . I daresay we do . . . You must listen to what I am going
to tell you very carefully. You must never reveal one word of it to a soul.
Do you understand?
Madre Yes, my lady.
Contessa If one word of this goes further than yourself, or to some others
who might have to know a little of what I say, in order to help you . . .
there will be no money.
Madre Yes, my lady.

Contessa And I shall have you killed and thrown in the canal. That can be done very easily in Venice. I could speak to the right man tonight, and you could be in a sack at the bottom of the lagoon by tomorrow evening. If you break even a fragment of my confidence, I swear to you, I will do it!

Madre You need not threaten me, my lady. I am a daughter of the Church, and I shall treat what you say as if it were said in Confession.

Contessa Don't make that your marker, priests can be bribed more easily than anyone I know!

Madre I cannot.

Contessa No, I don't think you can . . . I am younger than you. Something over thirty. And I am Venetian. But I was born poor. Almost poor enough to come here — except that both my parents were alive till I was ten. From that time on, I had to look after myself, on the streets of Venice. You understand what that means.

Madre Yes my lady, I do.

Contessa I was married to the Count for eleven years. I was his mistress for one year before that. That leaves thirteen years between. From the age of ten, till I was twenty-three I lived in Venice. I sang a little, played the guitar. I charmed men. At twenty-two I was beautiful, and I had managed to acquire a certain sophistication, well beyond my means. I wasn't a slut on the dockside selling my favours to deckhands and swabbers.

Madre No, my lady.

Contessa The Count fell desperately in love with me, and I with him. So desperately, that he wanted to marry me. Which never happens, as you know. For me it was a miracle, as though God himself had let His hand down from Heaven and lifted me out of the gutter.

Madre I'm sure it was no less, my lady.

Contessa But . . . unfortunately . . . I was pregnant. By the man I had been living with before the Count found me: and it was too late to abort the child. I feigned illness for a month — the Count was terrified for my life, — and I arranged to have the child, without him ever knowing. Well. I'm sure you can guess the rest.

Madre The child came here.

Contessa Yes. I kept her for a few days, that's all. You can imagine the anguish of letting her go. Or perhaps you can't.

Madre I think I can.

Contessa I left her at the grille, wrapped in a shawl, with a note begging you to look after her . . . and a small golden locket as a token of my love. I had no choice you see. I had to do it, or lose the only chance I was ever likely to have to climb out of the pit.

Madre I understand. When was this?

Contessa Just thirteen years ago this coming Summer. June the twenty-fifth. It was a Sunday. Three o'clock in the morning. Before dawn, but on the Lord's day, to be sure she would be safe in His hands.

Madre And you hope she is still here?

Contessa I know she is. She must be.

Madre I have to say that there is no certainty. Some children die, some run away, some are taken away, married, put to work, many things. But the records of the Pietà are very complete, a hundred times what you see in this room. And if she is still here, or ever came here, we will find her.

Contessa You must find her. You have the exact day, even the time. And the locket, a small golden heart on a chain.

Madre And if we do find her?

Contessa I shall take her away with me. My life is my own now, with palaces in Rome, Venice, Naples and Verona. I shall not marry again. But I want my daughter back.

Madre She will be nearly thirteen now.

Contessa I was at the concert yesterday. Although the girls were invisible, I felt sure she was there.

Madre It is most unlikely she would be part of the Coro, my lady. There are more than eight hundred girls who are not.

Contessa Oh no, I felt quite certain she was there. I was a singer for a time, and so was my mother. She is sure to be musical.

Madre We shall do our best. But it will take a few days.

Contessa I need not tell you how great my gratitude will be. I shall settle a great deal of money on the Pietà, if you have cared for my daughter and kept her safe all these years.

Madre I feel sure we shall have.

Contessa I can't stay any longer. I feel her presence, too close to endure.

Madre I understand.

Contessa And remember Sister Maria — Maddalena — no word of this. Or face down in the canal.

Madre The necessity will not arise, I promise you.

Contessa When will I see you again?

Madre Give us three days. Then come back, mid-morning.

Contessa Thank you.

Madre I am your servant, my lady. No thanks are required.

The Madre follows her out

The scene changes to the street in Venice, with the alleys, as before

Grimaldo enters, a tall, dark, fearsome Italian, down on his luck

Grimaldo Pazzo!

Pazzo enters, a short, unshaven, crafty Italian, even further down than Grimaldo

Pazzo Signore?

Grimaldo We are finally starving!

Pazzo We are, signore. My belly thinks my throat's cut.

Grimaldo We've tried everything. The military life, as gentlemen mercenary soldiers.

Pazzo We picked the wrong side. They plucked us naked as chickens.

Grimaldo The life of Commerce and Trade.

Pazzo We opened a bank that went bust, bought a fleet that sank, and sold wine that poisoned a whole Tuscan town. If they hadn't been in such agony, we'd never have got out alive.

Grimaldo We even tried the Church!
Pazzo Because everybody knows there's plenty of money in the Church. But the priests have got it all sown up!
Grimaldo And now we are here in Venice, in our last suit of clothes, and with boot-leather so thin that the cracks in the paving stones give us blisters.
Pazzo But we've come to the right place, signore. If you can't make money in Venice, you must be either deaf, blind or honest!
Grimaldo So, what shall we do, Pazzo?
Pazzo We could try murder. There's always plenty of call for that.
Grimaldo It's dangerous.
Pazzo Often terminally so. A short life, and a bloody one.
Grimaldo We could open a brothel.
Pazzo The market's glutted, prices falling, no profit margin. Anyway, there's too many in this city who'll do it for nothing.
Grimaldo Or run a string of high-class courtesans.
Pazzo There are sixteen thousand of those here already, signore, at last count.
Grimaldo Or fraud. Crooked deals, shady finance. You don't even need money for that, just a pen and a sheet of paper.
Pazzo And who will your clients be? Venetians! Those fellows'll take you to the cleaners and back before you even know your shirt's dirty.
Grimaldo What shall we do then, Pazzo? I am an Italian nobleman, I must eat!
Pazzo I'll tell you what. This city doesn't make anything any more, it doesn't trade anything any more, and yet it's rich! So what do you think it sells?
Grimaldo I don't know Pazzo, what does it sell?
Pazzo It sells itself! Tourism! Everybody comes here to see Venice. So what shall we sell them?
Grimaldo We'll sell them Venice!
Pazzo That's right!
Grimaldo Do you mean brick by brick?
Pazzo No, signore, you just wait and see. Look, here come a couple of likely clients. Every street corner they are, like berries on a bush. All you have to do is —
Grimaldo ⎱ (*together*) Pluck 'em!
Pazzo   ⎰

Milord and Bodger enter

Grimaldo and Pazzo move to one side, watching them

Milord Bodger!
Bodger Yes sir?
Milord My dear old Bodger!
Bodger What?
Milord It's happened!
Bodger Has it?

Milord I'm in love!

Bodger Not with me, you're not!

Milord Like a vision, like an angel, playing the fiddle and singing, as though this was Paradise and the eternal concert had begun!

Bodger You had me worried there for a moment.

Milord Bodger, how did you like the Cardinal's party?

Bodger Terrific. The wine was rich, the food was juicy, and so was the chambermaid.

Milord But the Art, Bodger, the music, all the Titians and Tintorettos, all the Cantatas and ripienos and ritornelli!

Bodger Was that the ice-cream? I saw they had different flavours.

Milord Bodger, you have the soul of a muckheap in a cowshed. Flies smell you for miles around.

Bodger I may do sir, but my body makes up for it. Ask the chambermaid.

Pazzo and Grimaldo come forward

Pazzo Signori, gentlemen, welcome to Venice!

Milord Good-afternoon.

Bodger (*aside*) Watch it, sir!

Pazzo You are a Dutchman.

Milord No I'm not!

Pazzo A German.

Milord No!

Pazzo French, Spanish.

Milord Certainly not!

Pazzo Swede, Austrian, Russian.

Milord I am an Englishman! Isn't that obvious?

Pazzo Of course you are! The English are the best actors in the world. They can be any man and every man at the same time. Whereas an Italian . . .

Milord Is always an Italian . . .

Pazzo Precisely. Can I introduce my master, the Count Grimaldo di Grimadli, from one of the oldest families in Italy.

Grimaldo Your servant, sir.

Bodger How old?

Pazzo So old, no-one remembers. His ancestors were Roman Senators.

Bodger What were your ancestors?

Pazzo Lost, signore, in the mists of time: like yours.

Bodger My dad was a blacksmith, moonlighting as a highwayman. It helped with the horses.

Milord Do you know Venice well?

Pazzo Signor Conte, do we know Venice well?

Grimaldo Every brick, signore, every stone! I was born here. I grew up here. Several of my palaces are here.

Milord Several, eh?

Grimaldo Others in Rome, Padua, Siena.

Milord And I suppose you know everybody too?

Grimaldo Only everybody worth knowing, signore. The rest are beneath my attention.

Pazzo But whoever you want to see in Venice, whatever you want to look at, or listen to, or buy, we, for a small fee, can arrange it for you.

Milord Bodger, we're in luck! This is just what we're looking for!

Bodger Watch out, sir. All Italians are crooks.

Milord That may be, Bodger: but all Englishmen are clever. We are decent, straightforward fellows, and we have the best navy in the world. The combination is unbeatable.

Grimaldo What can my servant get for you, signore? What are you in need of?

Milord Those girls, playing in the orchestra, last night at the Cardinal's, where can I find them?

Grimaldo Pazzo?

Pazzo At the Pietà, signore, where they live. Has one of them taken your fancy?

Milord She is an angel, when she sings it's like an immortal bird trilling in Heaven, and when she plays the violin ——

Bodger It's like a cat being strangled in an alley.

Pazzo Nothing could be simpler, signore. It will cost you two guineas.

Milord Two guineas? That's rather a lot.

Pazzo We must make a donation to the Pietà, signore, for the nuns, every time we pass the door. Is two guineas too much for you, signore?

Milord Oh no, not in the least, we're ——

Bodger Yes, it is, very expensive, isn't there a cheaper way? We're getting very short we are, we might have to get the boat back tomorrow.

Pazzo You get what you pay for in Venice, signore. Everything has its price.

Grimaldo Perhaps you do not need the services of a nobleman, signore? Perhaps a common gondolier will do?

Milord No, no, please! I want some pictures too, not all that religious stuff — we don't go for that sort of thing in England. What I like is views, from the hotel balcony, churches and things. To show people where I've been.

Pazzo You mean Canaletto, signore! And by the most fortunate chance, we have several in our lodgings.

Milord Do you hear that, Bodger! They've got several Canalettos in their lodgings!

Grimaldo (*aside*) You fool! We haven't.

Pazzo (*aside*) We'll get some painted tonight. There are unemployed artists in every cafe in Venice, and every one of them can do a Canaletto!

Milord And what about music, can you get me some concertos too?

Pazzo Concertos, cantatas, operas, you name it, we get it.

Milord What was he called last night . . .? Viv Aldi!

Pazzo Ah, the Reverend Don Antonio? Would you like to meet him perhaps?

Milord Bodger, did you hear that? We're going to meet Viv Aldi!

Pazzo (*aside*) Is he in town?

Grimaldo (*aside*) No, he's not!

Pazzo (*aside*) Anyone'll do, as long as he's red-haired and got asthma.

Grimaldo (*aside*) He's supposed to be a musician.
Pazzo (*aside*) All right, a street fiddler with a wig!
Milord But first of all, that wonderful girl! I must meet her.
Grimaldo This way signore. I will lead. You may pay your two guineas to
my man.
Milord Now?
Pazzo We prefer payment in advance, signore, if you don't mind. We need
it to bribe the doorman.
Milord Oh yes, of course. Come on Bodger, don't lag behind! We're
in luck!
Bodger This is going to cost us a lot of money!

They all go off. Bodger lingering for his last line

*The scene changes. The stage is divided into three areas. The centre back
area represents the Madre's office, as before.* DR *We see a plain bed, as in
a small cell or dormitory.* DL *a similar plain bed. It is a late evening*

The Madre writes in a huge ledger at her desk, by the light of a lamp

Sister Teresa comes in

Sister Teresa Madre . . .
Madre Come in, Sister Teresa . . .
Sister Teresa Sister Annunciata says she is sorry she hasn't found the
information you asked for yet.
Madre It is very important.
Sister Teresa But she is sure she has found the right ledger, and the chest
with the things. She will tell you as soon as she knows.
Madre Good. Have all the hysterics finished?
Sister Teresa Yes, Madre. It was Sister Angelica.
Madre I know who it was. The girl is mad with love. For a tenor from
the opera.
Sister Teresa She cries all the time, Madre.
Madre Well. We all cry, Sister.
Sister Teresa Yes, Madre.
Madre I came here because I wanted peace, and the religious life. I
sometimes think there are more love affairs going on within these walls
than in the whole of Venice. God is mocked daily, under his own roof.
Sister Teresa Yes, Madre.
Madre I have often thought of leaving, joining some more enclosed,
contemplative order. But I couldn't leave the girls.
Sister Teresa No, Madre.
Madre We must live with the world as we find it, Sister. More than half the
nuns have no vocation, and have simply been dumped here because their
fathers couldn't afford to marry them. Will Sister Angelica be all right?
Sister Teresa I don't know, Madre.
Madre We might as well let her out for a week. Get it over. During
Carnival no-one will notice.
Sister Teresa She may not come back, Madre.

Madre So much the better. We'll wait for a week or so. If he's an opera singer, he'll have forgotten all about her by then, unless he's quite untypical of the breed . . . When I first became Madre di Coro, Sister, I was so shocked by what I saw in the convent, that I went to the Mother Superior to tell her. I learned later that she had had at least three lovers in the last two years. Not all of them men. The only thing that really touches the hearts of half the nuns here, Sister Teresa, is the Theatre, and Fashion. And love of course. The unspiritual kind.

Sister Teresa Yes, Madre.

Madre You keep your own counsel, Sister: which is probably wise.

Sister Teresa The other thing, Madre, is that the young English Milord has been again, begging to be allowed to see Maestra Anna-Maria.

Madre He's not the first. But she has always refused. As is her right.

Sister Teresa He is very insistent, Madre.

Madre And he is also very rich. I took the opportunity to speak to him the first time. A pleasant enough boy, rather silly. She could do a great deal worse.

Sister Teresa She lives for the violin, Madre. It's all that matters to her.

Madre That may be. But in two months she must leave here, and her violin won't help her then. All things considered, she had better see him. I think so. Send her to me . . . this evening, before she goes to bed.

Sister Teresa Yes Madre . . .

The Lights fade on the Madre's room, and come up on the bed DL

Prudenza, Pellegrina and Michelotta enter in their shifts, ready for bed, lit by oil lights or rush lights

Prudenza There's two nights next week with no concerts. We'll do it then.

Pellegrina How will we get out?

Prudenza Through the back gateway, on to the little square. The doorman lets anyone in and out for money.

Michelotta There are more cloaked figures going in and out there at night than through the main gate!

Prudenza You just have to be careful that you don't bump into too many masked nuns!

Pellegrina Did you see him last night at the concert?

Prudenza See him!

Pellegrina Isn't he beautiful! I had nothing to do in the second half, and I watched him all the time, leaning against the pillar! He's so slim and elegant, in that beautiful coat and tight trousers! And his face is the face of a young god! It made me go quite shaky!

Michelotta Apollo. Or Orpheus!

Prudenza But I did more than see him!

Pellegrina What do you mean?

Prudenza I persuaded one of the Cardinal's footmen to take him a message! On half a page of the concerto where I had nothing to play!

Pellegrina Did he answer it?

Pellegrina He couldn't send a note himself. But I watched him when he got mine, and he lowered his head and smiled! It was quite clear. Our eyes met!

Michelotta What did you say in the note?

Prudenza That I would be in St Mark's Square, under the colonnade, by Florian's Coffee House, when it gets dark. And I will be wearing a red devil mask!

Pellegrina But what will he be wearing?

Michelotta He couldn't say, could he, if he only nodded!

Prudenza Oh, I'll find him. I'll recognize those gorgeous legs anywhere!

Paulina enters with a box which contains costumes and masks

Paulina I've got them, look!

Michelotta Oh, wonderful!

Pellegrina There's your red devil. And I claim the Nereid!

Michelotta I shall have to have this droopy long-nosed one!

Paulina I wouldn't. It's a bad omen!

Michelotta Oh, you are terrible!

Prudenza Will they be safe here?

Paulina Back in the box and behind the bed.

Pellegrina All we have to do now is bribe the doorman!

Prudenza That's the easy bit.

Michelotta Will we stay out all night?

Prudenza Can't get back in, so we'll have to!

The Lights cross-fade to the DR *area, where Candida and Silvia are sitting on the bed in their night-shifts, or getting undressed down to the shift. The scene is lit by a rush light, or small lamp*

Candida Anna's a long time with the Madre. I wonder what she wants?

Silvia Can't you guess?

Candida No.

Silvia She's got a client.

Candida What?

Silvia She's fixed up a man for her. A respectable Venetian banker, like with Angelotta, two years ago. So another fiddler's gone, and there's another bag of ducats under the Madre's bed. It'll be your turn next.

Candida Me? I couldn't possibly! No, I couldn't!

Silvia What are you going to do then? Be a nun?

Candida I don't know. It's so frightening outside. The way the men look at you.

Silvia I don't mind the ones who merely undress you with their eyes. It's the ones who lick you all over as well I can't stand.

Candida It's so much safer here.

Silvia Well. It might. Or it might not be. When some of those nuns get a pretty young thing like you safely inside the convent . . . Anything might happen!

Anna-Maria enters

Candida Anna . . . What is it? . . . Are you all right?

Anna-Maria Yes. I'm all right.

Silvia Well tell us then. How rich is he?

Anna-Maria Very. Very rich indeed.

Silvia God bless you child, some people always have it easy!

Anna-Maria I don't know.

Silvia What happened? Tell us!

Anna-Maria The Madre told me there is an English Milord . . .

Silvia English! Very stiff and strict, the English. Not as bad as the Germans, but pretty awful!

Candida Is he handsome?

Anna-Maria I haven't seen him. The Madre says he's good-looking, and good-hearted . . . and very much in love with me.

Silvia Goodbye, Anna-Maria my darling. Send us a letter from England.

Anna-Maria And he wants to marry me, and take me with him.

Candida To be an English Milady!

Silvia Not only can she sing, not only can she play the violin a little . . .

Candida So that all Europe falls on its knees before her . . .

Silvia She also draws an English Milord out of the hat! When are you going, before the end of Carnival or after?

Anna-Maria I don't know.

Silvia Sooner rather than later. Don't give him a chance to change his mind.

Anna-Maria I mean . . . I don't know that I'm going.

Silvia You don't know? Why not?

Anna-Maria I don't know that I want to go to England . . . or become an English Milady.

Silvia You don't . . .? She's mad, this girl is mad!

Candida Why not?

Anna-Maria I don't know anything about England. Is there any music there?

Silvia Music! As if it matters! Here is an English nobleman! You'll never get anything like him here. Italian aristocrats don't marry orphan girls from the convent, even if they can play the violin! The best you'll get here is a dreary merchant, if you're lucky. This one has lands, houses, peasants, horses! You will live in a palace, and have servants at your beck and call!

Anna-Maria I don't want that! I want to play the violin. Don't you understand Silvia, you must know what I mean. You are the greatest cellist I have ever seen, you are better than any of us here! Why does Maestro Vivaldi write you such wonderful concertos? Last night was so passionate, and so difficult, and you made it seem so easy and so musical! And then the slow movement was so sad, that falling phrase, like tears,

and you played it like someone weeping her heart out in public. How can
you do that, and not care!

Silvia (*with real pain*) Not care . . . !

A pause

Candida What's the matter, Silvia?

Anna-Maria What did I say?

Silvia (*bitterly*) Did you notice how long a pause there was between the first
and second half last night? Over an hour.

Candida They gave us some food. I even had a glass of wine.

Silvia Well. You can guess where I was.

Anna-Maria The Cardinal invited you to his private chamber. You went
with two nuns.

Silvia The nuns stopped at the door. Were stopped, by two priests.

Candida You were alone with him?

Silvia For nearly an hour. He's old, and fat, and disgusting. But . . . at
least I don't have to make the choice between the nunnery and the streets
now . . .

Anna-Maria Silvia . . . !

Silvia I shall have my own little house, just off the Grand Canal, beyond the
Rialto, with my own servants. I can even take my cello with me to keep
me company! I shall see the Cardinal twice a week. It will all be most
discreet, as befits a Prince of the Church. That's a good price, don't you
think? A good bargain I made?

Anna-Maria Silvia ——

Silvia That's why I played with such passion, Anna-Maria. That's why I
wept so convincingly.

Candida It's horrible.

Silvia No it isn't. It's brilliant. I've won.

Anna-Maria But how can you stop playing? You play more beautifully
than anyone in Italy: and that means the world! How can you give it
up?

Silvia I can give it up because it's that or my life! I have no choice: and
neither do you. Marry your English Milord, marry him quickly. At least
he's young and good-looking. England is a filthy, cold place, but you will
be your own mistress, and so will I here. You should be congratulating
me. I'm safe! I can begin to live!

Anna-Maria Without music.

Silvia It doesn't matter to me that much! What is music? You've already
said it. Just a kind of weeping out loud. Only children do that. It's time
we grew up.

The Lights fade on the DR *section and come up* C *on Madre's office*

Sister Teresa enters

Sister Teresa Madre. Sister Annunciata is here.

Madre Oh . . . come in Sister . . .

Sister Annunicata enters

Sister Annunciata I'm sorry it took so long, Madre. It's almost time for the bell.

Madre But you've found the child.

Sister Annunciata Yes, Madre.

Madre Come in, Sister Teresa, don't stand at the door. (*To Annunciata*) You're quite sure it's her?

Sister Annunciata Yes Madre, quite sure. I've copied all the entries. And I have these things which were left with her.

Madre Excellent. Well, tell me!

Sister Annunciata Well, there is a record of a child left at the grille, June the twenty-fifth, thirteen years ago. There was a shawl with the child and a locket, a heart on a chain: and a note. The child was christened Abandonnata.

Madre Excellent, Sister Annunciata, what could be better! Abandonnata. She is not one of the Coro. Which of the Commoners' Halls is she in?

Sister Annunciata Madre, that's not all.

Madre What else?

Sister Annunciata She died, Madre. Two weeks later.

Madre Died?

Sister Annunciata Yes, Madre. It's quite clear in the records. The things were in the box kept for the belongings of dead children.

Madre You are quite sure, Sister?

Sister Annunciata Quite sure, Madre. There is no possibility of a mistake.

Madre A double tragedy. The Contessa was about to give us a great deal of money. Which we badly need.

Sister Annunciata It's quite clear, Madre because it was an exceptional week. There were three baby girls left at the grille in eight days. She was the second. The first was on the twenty-second, the third on the thirtieth.

Madre Three girls. At the same time?

Sister Annunciata Yes, Madre.

Madre Who?

Sister Annunciata The first was christened Ignota, Madre, and the third Perduta.

Madre Perduta! Our little copyist!

Sister Annunciata Yes, Madre.

Madre Ignota, the other one?

Sister Teresa She ran away, Madre, when she was ten.

Madre Oh yes, I remember. A terrifying child! God knows where she is now . . . And this is the shawl, and the locket?

Sister Annunciata Yes, Madre. And the note.

Madre "For God's sake take care of my child." We failed to do that, didn't we.

Sister Annunciata The child was always sickly, Madre, the record makes that quite clear. It was hardly ever alive.

Madre Poor woman.

Sister Annunciata What shall we do, Madre?

Madre Replace the ledgers. Leave the things with me.

A bell begins to ring

Sister Teresa Time for prayers, Madre.
Madre Yes. We must all pray with a special fervour tonight, Sisters. In such a dreadful time, we all need guidance.
Sister Teresa ⎫
Sister Annunciata ⎬ *(together)* Yes Madre . . .

The Lights come up. As the bell rings all three groups, R, L and C kneel and pray. The Lights slowly fade on them

The scene changes to the reception room or parlour of the convent of the Pietà, a large open room, split down the middle by a wall which contains two openings like huge windows, only instead of glass they contain a wide mesh iron grille, the holes being four or five inches square. Hands can be touched through them, and lips too, I daresay. On the side within the convent a large curtain cuts off any further vision. There are chairs set both sides of the grille for people to converse together, so that, although privacy is not possible, a certain kind of intimacy is

In the public part of the room, there are all kinds of people, a ragged boy who plays the sopranino recorder, for two tumblers who perform as he plays, a boy with thee puppets, and standing on one side of the room, a Punch and Judy booth. There is also a ragged girl who sells ribbon and lace from a tray, and three or four ragged boys sitting round the walls, apparently doing nothing, who are probably pickpockets. While the room is empty of the public, they all sit round the room bored, but as soon as anyone enters, the whole group bursts into activity

There is a momentary pause, and then Milord enters, led by Pazzo, with Bodger following

Immediately, the recorder player begins to play, the tumblers tumble, the girl comes forward with her tray, and the boy begins to make his puppets dance. The opening speeches are played more or less together

Girl Buy some ribbons and laces, signori, for your mistresses, they will love you for ever with these in their hair!
Puppet Boy Watch the puppets dance, signori, and for a groat they will perform a play!
Punch and Judy Man Come and see the famous Mr Punch beating his wife, signori, no better entertainment in all Venice!
Puppet Boy The story of the Prince, the Princess and the Gondolier!
Tumbler Don't forget the tumblers, sir, remember the acrobats!
Milord Good God, where are we? Bartholomew Fair?
Pazzo No, signore, this is the Parlour of the Convent of the Pietà ——
Bodger I've seen duller market days in Leicester.
Pazzo —— the nuns' Reception Room, where they meet their friends and lovers.
Bodger Their lovers? I thought they took vows of chastity?
Pazzo But what are vows, signore? Soldiers take vows of loyalty, and

change sides if they are losing, dukes takes vows of fealty to kings, and murder them in their palaces, and bankers take vows of honesty. It is the world, signore. We didn't make it, but we must live in it.

Milord But what are all these people doing here?

Pazzo Selling, sir, what else? Lots of people come here, some of them rich. In such places there will always be people with things to sell.

Milord Just us at the moment.

Pazzo That is because it's early, signore. After midday people will be queueing up to take their turn at the grille, and these people will be making money. Or stealing it.

Milord Stealing?

Pazzo Keep your eye on those ragged boys, signore, with nothing to sell. They will have your watch and your wallet if you give them half a chance.

The ragged boys move suddenly in a bunch, and brush past Pazzo and Milord

Keep your hands in your pockets, signore! Like this.

Milord Oh yes, I see . . .

Bodger Oh look, the Punch and Judy's beginning! I love Punch and Judy.

Punch and Judy Man "I am the famous Punchinello. And this is Judy my wife!"

Punch hits Judy

Bodger That's the way, Mr Punch, you give her what for!

A crowd of ragged and half-starved children of both sexes runs in noisily, and gathers by one of the grilles, shouting

Sister Teresa emerges from behind the curtain with a basket of bread rolls, which she proceeds to give them through the grille

They eat greedily, and wait, hoping for more

Milord What's happening now?

Pazzo These are the starving children. They come in two or three times a day. The nuns give them bread.

Milord What do they do if the nuns don't give them bread?

Pazzo They starve, signore.

Sister Teresa That's all, there isn't any more . . .

The noisy crowd of children immediately begins to leave, in search of another hand-out

Milord is immediately attacked again by the various hucksters, who gather round him with their wares

Puppet Boy The play, signore, let me show you the play . . .

Milord Oh, well . . . I don't know . . .

Puppet Boy (*performing*) This is the story of the famous Prince of Venice, the Princess, and the Gondolier . . .

The recorder player is beginning to play, the girl is trying to sell ribbons, and Punch and Judy is progressing. Pazzo gets the attention of Sister Teresa as she is going

Pazzo The English Milord is here, to see Maestr'Anna-Maria.
Sister Teresa Oh . . . yes . . . I'll get her.

Sister Teresa goes behind the curtain

Punch and Judy Man "Oh Mr Punch, how can you treat me so bad?" "It's easy. I just take my stick and do this!"
Bodger That's the way, Mr Punch! He'll kill her in a minute!

Pazzo turns to the hucksters and yells ferociously

Pazzo Go away, scum, filth, leave the English Milord alone! If you sit quietly at the wall, he will give you a shower of money! Won't you, Milord!
Milord Well, I'd rather give it to them for entertaining me ——

The hucksters try to begin again, but Pazzo intimidates them

—— but yes, of course I will!

Sister Teresa appears from behind the curtain with Anna-Maria and Sister Annunciata. Anna sits on the stool behind the grille. The two nuns stand behind her

Sister Teresa Signore, Maestr'Anna-Maria is here.
Pazzo Silence, filth, while the English Milord speaks!

The hucksters all scurry to the walls and sit in silence

Bodger Oh, don't stop the Punch and Judy show! Oh . . . well . . . yes.

Milord sits facing Anna-Maria. He is awestruck, almost speechless at seeing her so close

Milord I . . . er . . .
Anna-Maria You asked to see me, Milord?
Milord I . . . You played beautifully. At the Cardinal's.
Anna-Maria Thank you, Milord.
Milord And . . . sang beautifully too . . . But now I see you close up, without your violin . . .
Anna-Maria You see a body, signore. But the soul is absent.
Milord Oh . . . well. I wasn't going to say that. The body is . . . wonderful . . . on its own.
Anna-Maria I believe you know . . . I must leave the Pietà.
Milord I've met the woman who looks after you all . . . I mean, the chief nun . . .
Anna-Maria La Madre di Coro.
Milord Yes, I suppose that's the one . . . I want . . . to take you back to England.
Anna-Maria Signore?

Milord I mean, no, I want to marry you. Here. Well, no, I mean in England. I have a very big house, in Leicestershire, and two town houses in London, and a villa in Middlesex . . . lots of land, cows, sheep. Farms. Forests . . . rivers . . . all sorts. You will be very happy in England. And very rich.

Anna-Maria I know nothing about England. What do you do there?

Milord Do? Ah, well . . . We ride. We eat . . . a lot. Balls of course, we have balls. Go to London for the season. Play cricket.

Anna-Maria What is . . . cricket . . .?

Milord Ah well . . . how long have we got? . . . Well, no, it's a game English gentlemen play with their servants, on the grass. I mean, there's two wickets, one at each end, and a bat and ball . . . and the two captains toss up at the beginning, and . . . Perhaps you don't have cricket in Italy.

Anna-Maria I don't think so.

Milord No, well, Venice. You wouldn't.

Anna-Maria Do you have music?

Milord (*relieved*) Music, oh, good heavens, yes! The opera in London. Italian opera!

Anna-Maria Which composers?

Milord Oh, well, let me see. Handel! He's Italian. Lots of others. Can't remember their names. We go to see the singers really, and to chat to our friends.

Anna-Maria And your house?

Milord What about my house?

Anna-Maria Music in your house?

Milord Oh yes. Every now and again. I play the fiddle myself.

Anna-Maria (*smiling enthusiastically*) You play the violin?

Milord Oh yes, the Chaplain plays the harpsichord, and there's one of the servants plays the gamba, and the chap from the cowshed plays the serpent. Sometimes, when we have a dance, I play myself, though my mother doesn't approve. Jigs and hornpipes, and good old *Sir Roger de Coverley*!

Anna-Maria Who is he?

Milord No, No. It's not a person. It's a tune.

Anna-Maria I don't think I know this music.

Milord No, well, it's English. Very English. Not the sort of thing you play. I'm going to buy lots of that. Lots and lots of it, concertos and cantatas, while I'm here . . . You're so beautiful I can't stop looking at you.

Anna-Maria If I went to England, would I be able to play?

Milord Of course! Bring your violin. We'll play together!

Anna-Maria No, I mean concerts. With an orchestra. Do you have a Court Orchestra?

Milord What, in Leicestershire?

Anna-Maria In your house.

Milord Well. Not as far as I know. I've never seen one. It is a big house. I might have missed it.

Anna-Maria Could I play with your orchestra? Is that the custom in England?

Milord Well, er . . . you mean in public?

Anna-Maria For concerts.

Milord For friends you mean. Like the Duke of Chandos at Cannons. But, not in public, for money, no. One's wife can't play in public. I mean. That isn't done.

Anna-Maria No . . . here it is the same. It is very kind of you to ask me. I am an orphan, like we all are here, and I have no friends but the nuns and my violin.

Milord You have me now.

Anna-Maria Thank you, signore . . . Will you . . . please allow me to think. Just a few days.

Milord Of course! Take your time! I shall be here for months yet! When can I see you again? Preferably not with this grille between us.

Anna-Maria I will be playing at the Grand Duke of Tuscany's ball tonight. Will you be there?

Milord It will take the Grand Duke and all his armies to stop me!

Anna-Maria Thank you, signore.

Milord No indeed. Thank you.

Gracefully she withdraws behind the curtain with the two nuns

Milord is dazed, shattered, gobsmacked

Oh Bodger! She is an angel! I'm lost!

Bodger Sir, haven't you forgotten something?

Milord What?

Bodger You're married.

Milord We're going to have to do something about that, Bodger! We really are. She's wonderful! I love her to distraction! I *must* marry her!

Bodger Well the least you can do, sir, is ask your wife.

Grimaldo enters, grimly

Grimaldo Pazzo!

Pazzo Signore?

Grimaldo Outside, there is a Frenchman who wants to meet a large number of ballet dancers. Do we know any ballet dancers?

Pazzo No, signore. But I do know where we can find some good-looking sailors.

Grimaldo He wants ballet dancers, not sailors!

Pazzo If he's a Frenchman, signore, he won't know the difference.

Pazzo hurries out with Grimaldo

All the hucksters begin again

Bodger Oh good, the Punch and Judy's beginning again.

Milord (*slightly nervously*) Bodger, I think we ought to get out while the going's good.

Bodger He said you were going to give them some money, sir. I don't think

they'll be very pleased if you don't.
Milord Quite right . . . (*He feels in his pocket*) Bodger!
Bodger What?
Milord My purse. It's been lifted!
Bodger Don't let on, whatever you do.
Milord How much have you got in your pocket?
Bodger Five pence. All in pennies.
Milord English or Italian?
Bodger English.
Milord It'll have to do. Give it to me. (*He holds up the money in his closed fist*) Here we are. For you. Catch!

He throws the money in the air. They all dive for it

Run!

Bodger and Milord go off, and the Lights fade on the scrum

The scene changes to an ante room in the Grand Duke of Tuscany's palace. Off stage a formal minuet is being played and danced

All the girls come on stage, in their white habits, wearing their cloaks, and carrying their instruments. They talk together as they remove their cloaks and put them on chairs. Perduta hands out folders of music

Maestro Vandini comes in with Maestra Luciana

Luciana Where is the Madre? She said she would be here before the concert began!
Vandini Well, it doesn't matter. We can play without her.
Luciana But where is she, why is she not here when she is supposed to be?
Vandini The Governors called her to a special meeting this afternoon. She said she would take a fast gondola as soon as she could.
Luciana The Governors? Why?
Vandini I have no idea . . .

Vandini talks to some of the girls, while Luciana singles out Lucietta, for some last-minute instruction. Anna-Maria, Silvia and Candida are near the front of the stage

Silvia Will he be here tonight?
Anna-Maria Yes, I think so.
Candida What's he like? Did you like him?
Anna-Maria I think so. He's a pleasant man.
Silvia Well, what does liking have to do with it? Is he better than the nunnery?
Anna-Maria Yes. Better than that.
Silvia So. Brava. I'll throw rose petals at your wedding.
Anna-Maria Yes, I suppose so . . .

Sister Teresa enters from the Grand Salon

Sister Teresa Maestro Vandini, the dancing is over . . .
Vandini Ah . . . My children . . . my children!
Sister Teresa And the Madre is here.

The Madre enters, still wearing her warm outdoor cloak

Madre Be quiet, all of you!

They fall silent instantly

We can hear your chatter in the Grand Salon! Compose yourselves to play. Is everything ready?
Vandini Yes, Madre. You have all your music in the correct order?
Perduta Yes, Maestro, they have. I checked every folder.
Vandini Good. Maestra Anna-Maria, you are leading the orchestra tonight?
Anna-Maria Yes, Maestro.
Vandini And Lucietta leading the continuo?
Lucietta Yes, Maestro.
Vandini So we are truthfully superfluous. We can sit back and listen, as if we merely loved music, without the burden of making it!
Sister Teresa They're ready now, Maestro
Madre All right, Maestr'Anna, lead them in. Remember, don't begin till the Grand Duke's master of ceremonies gives you the signal. It'll be at least five minutes.
Anna-Maria Yes, Madre . . .
Madre Off you go then.
Vandini Good luck, my children, daughters of the Muse !

The girls file into the Grand Salon. There is some applause, but little change in the general level of talk from the duke's guests

The three elders look at each other, and the two teachers prepare to follow

Madre Maestra Luciana, Maestro Vandini! Wait here a moment please.

The two teachers stop and return enquiringly

Vandini Madre?
Luciana What is it, Madre?

There is a pause. The Madre is embarrassed

Madre Dear Luciana . . . I have some bad news for you.

Luciana freezes before she speaks

Luciana What?
Madre The Governors called me to a special meeting. They are making great changes. To save money, they say, but it seems to me to be purely destructive . . .
Luciana What? What is it?
Madre They will not renew your contract to teach organ and harpsichord. From Easter.

A pause. No-one speaks

Luciana But . . . what . . . ?

Madre I did all I could. I argued against them.

Luciana But who will teach my pupils? There will be no-one. I have been here since I was a little girl. Forty years.

Madre They say Lucietta can teach as well: and that only one organist is needed.

Luciana It isn't true! It isn't. She is a beginner!

Vandini Oh, Maestra, my dear . . . this is a disaster for all of us.

Luciana Where shall I go? What shall I do? I've been here all my life!

Quite suddenly Vivaldi enters, in a rush. He is a little over forty, a man of consumingly vast energy, and powerful temper. In fact he suffers from asthma, and always carries a stick with him to lean on when he gets out of breath, which he occasionally does, though not often when he is really worked up. He has a ruddy complexion, and wisps of his red hair are visible under his wig. He is in a fury

Vivaldi Vandini, there you are!

Vandini Maestro Vivaldi! How long have you been in Venice?

Vivaldi About two hours. And the first thing I hear is that at the Grand Duke of Tuscany's assembly, all the music is to be my concertos!

Vandini Yes Don Antonio, a great honour.

Vivaldi You can have my share of the honour, Vandini, how much money did you get out of him?

Vandini Money?

Vivaldi For me, for my music!

Vandini Reverend Don Antonio, the concertos are the property of the Pietà . . .

Vivaldi Of course they are, but when you play them at the special request of the Grand Duke, I expect a substantial present. Ten or fifteen ducats at least!

Madre Don Antonio, no-one asked him.

Vivaldi Then you should have done! You have no right to use my music as though it were your own property! It is mine, Madre, I wrote it for the Pietà, not for public concerts in every salon in Venice! I shall march up to the Grand Duke when the applause is echoing round his great chamber, and in the most courteous manner possible, I shall indicate that some gift would be appropriate! The heir to the Medici can afford to pay a poor Venetian musician, whatever else he can do. My best wishes to you, old friend, and to you, Madre, and to you, Maestra Luciana. Will they play well tonight?

Madre I'm sure they will, Don Antonio.

Vandini What happened to you, Don Antonio? We heard you were in Prague?

Vivaldi I was. But there is not enough money to be made from opera there. They paid me fifty ducats for a whole opera, and spent a thousand on the castrato's helmet! I got out with my skin just about intact, but it was time

to leave. I shall stage a season of new operas here in the Summer, at the
Teatro San'Angelo.
Vandini Ah, it will be good to have you back after so long . . .
Vivaldi Anyway, you know why I am here. I am to be Maestro di Coro
again. The Governors wrote to Prague and asked me.
Vandini What?
Madre It's true. They told me tonight. I would have told you later.
Vivaldi Why all the glum faces? Did you not know? Well, nobody told me,
of course, they expect me to know these things by instinct! Don't worry,
old friend, you aren't to be booted out into the square. You are to teach
cello still. And you can play for me in the Summer, write some of the
recitatives too, to save my time.
Vandini Ah, thank you, Maestro.
Vivaldi But I do need money, every penny I can get. So the Duke must pay
for his pleasures.

*The music begins in the Salon. The "Spring" concerto, from "The Four
Seasons"*

Ah. How did I guess! If I had ten ducats every time this music was played,
I could retire and live in a castle. But. Everyone enjoys my music, and I
get what I can beg!

Madre is comforting Luciana. Vivaldi doesn't notice

Madre Don't cry, my child. We shall do something. We shall manage
something.
Luciana Where else can a woman teach the organ?
Madre We shall think of something.
Vivaldi Well. I seem to have cast a gloomy shadow. Shall I go back to
Prague, and tell the Governors to go to Hell? No, unfortunately I can't.
I need the money, and at the moment it can only be made here.

The solo music begins

Ah. The birds are singing well tonight. Who is playing?
Vandini Maestr'Anna-Maria.
Vivaldi Ah yes. The child is a master. We can teach her nothing. I suppose
she must be leaving soon?
Madre After the Carnival.
Vivaldi Have you arranged something. Is she to be married?
Madre I hope so.
Vivaldi The best thing. Get her to the church, and pregnant. Before she
does us all out of work. Thank God she's only a girl, eh Vandini? Or
where would the next meal come from?

They go into the Grand Salon together, laughing and talking

Madre Will you come in, Luciana?
Luciana No. I can't. I'll listen from here.

The Madre goes in to the Grand Salon

Luciana slowly sits on a chair, amid all the cast-off cloaks and instrument cases, as the music sweeps in from the next room. She lowers her head and cries, sobbing uncontrollably like an injured child

CURTAIN

ACT II

When the CURTAIN *rises we see the Madre's room in the Pietà*

The Madre is on stage with Sister Annunciata. Neither speaks

Sister Teresa enters

Sister Teresa The Contessa is here, Madre.
Madre Tell her . . . to wait just a moment.
Sister Teresa To wait, Madre?
Madre Just a moment.

Sister Teresa goes

Sister Annunciata What are you going to do?
Madre There is a mother who has lost her child. A child who has lost her
mother. What should I do?
Sister Annunciata But, Madre ——
Madre What are we talking about, Sister Annunciata? Strokes made by a
pen on a page, which may or may not be accurate.
Sister Annunciata There's no reason to think they are not, Madre.
Madre Nor any reason to think they are. There are three hundred years of
entries in those ledgers. Do you imagine there are no mistakes in all that
time? That poor woman needs her child. And all the children here need
parents. What would we achieve for either by telling them the child died?
Nothing but pain. Perduta will have to leave us eventually, and will never
have another chance like this. This is a miracle, Sister, and we must not
reject miracles when they are offered.
Sister Annunciata It isn't true, Madre.
Madre What is truth, Sister Annunciata . . . ? Pen strokes in a book? Or
the chance of happiness?
Sister Annunciata And a substantial gift, no doubt.

Madre is angered

Madre (*quietly*) You speak above your place, Sister. The whole of Venice
may be corrupt. You may be corrupt. But I am not! I remind you as a nun
you are under obedience to your superiors, and in this matter, I am your
superior. I command you to keep silent!
Sister Annunciata Yes, Madre.
Madre Tell Sister Teresa to send the Contessa in. And wait yourself in the
ante room.
Sister Annunciata Yes, Madre.

*The Contessa enters, shown in by Sister Teresa, who immediately leaves.
She looks pale and nervous*

Contessa Madre . . .
Madre My lady.
Contessa You have some news for me.
Madre Yes.
Contessa (*her face lighting up*) You've found my child. You have! I can tell from the look on your face! You've found her!
Madre I believe we have . . . Our little Perduta. Our lost one.
Contessa Perduta . . . She is found now. I have found her. Who gave her that name?
Madre One of my predecessors, my lady.
Contessa I shall keep it. She could not have been better named. It is a kind of miracle, Madre, isn't it. After all these years.
Madre Yes my lady, it is.
Contessa When can I see her?
Madre I have to tell you, my lady . . .
Contessa What?
Madre There can never be . . . absolute certainty. They say a father can never be quite sure of his paternity: and a mother whose child has been lost is in the same position. All we can say . . . is that the evidence is there.
Contessa But the day I left her . . . the note, the locket and shawl . . .?
Madre Yes my lady, we have found them . . . I say only what I must say when these occasions arise — and they are rare enough, rarer than we would wish. There is no certainty in any of the things of this world. The only absolute truth is with God, and in Heaven, not in Venice.
Contessa That is true, Madre, of spiritual things. But we have the locket, the shawl! There can't be any possibility of error!
Madre No, my lady. Very likely not.
Contessa Is she here? Can I see her now?
Madre Yes, she is.
Contessa Does she know?
Madre Yes. I told her myself.
Contessa What did she say?
Madre Almost nothing. She was dazed. They all make up stories about their parents all the time. But they never think they will come true, and when they do, it changes everything. But she is one of our very liveliest girls. I've no doubt she will be herself again by now.
Contessa Let me see her. Please.
Madre I'll bring her in.

Madre goes out

During the short pause while she is off stage, the Contessa walks quietly across the room, in an agony of expectation and fear

Madre enters with Perduta, who looks much paler and more subdued than usual. She carries a small bundle

There she is, my lady.

Perduta (*curtsying*) Good-morning, my lady.
Contessa Good-morning.
Madre I shall attend you in the ante room.

Madre goes

The woman and the girl look at each other, not knowing what to say, feeding on each other's physical reality after so many years of imagination

Perduta I am called Perduta here. I have no other name. The Madre has told me you are my mother.
Contessa Yes. I believe I am.
Perduta She gave me these things for you. (*Perduta hands her the bundle, the shawl and the locket*)
Contessa Oh, yes. Yes. (*She is near tears*) There is no question . . . There was a note too?
Perduta The Madre gave me no note, my lady.
Contessa No . . . well. Destroyed years ago, I daresay . . . You were wrapped in this tiny shawl. The locket was round your neck. May I put it there again?
Perduta Yes, my lady.

The Contessa replaces it with great emotion and tact, taking care not to touch the child

Contessa You must wear it there for ever.

There is a pause, the Contessa full of an emotion Perduta cannot share. She watches with a kind of fearful curiosity, aware that her whole life is changed, but not yet sure how to react

Perduta Did you really leave me at the grille?
Contessa Yes. I can never ask forgiveness enough . . . But if I hadn't done so . . . you would probably have died.
Perduta Why didn't you want to keep me: when you were so rich?
Contessa I wasn't rich then. And I did want to keep you. But I couldn't.

Pause

Perduta Am I to go with you now?
Contessa Yes, soon. I hope so.
Perduta Are you *very* rich?
Contessa I am rich, yes. You are my only child. Your life will be very different. You will have everything you want. You will never have to work.
Perduta I have always dreamed of my mother finding me. And in my dreams it was always someone like you. Rich and beautiful.
Contessa I'm very glad. Your dream has come true.
Perduta But it was just a dream. I never thought it would happen.

Pause

Contessa What's the matter?
Perduta I . . . I am the chief copyist. I make all the parts for the orchestra

to play, and the soloists too, Maestra Silvia and all the others.

Contessa That must be very hard work.

Perduta But I don't just copy. I have studied counterpoint and harmony. The others all tease me because I can't play any instrument except the keyboard, but I know more about music than any of them. I have to be able to adapt the music to suit our players if it was written for other instruments. I have to write bits too sometimes, to make everything fit.

Contessa That's all finished now. You need never do anything like that again.

Perduta No, but . . . what *shall* I do then?

Contessa You need do nothing at all. You will be my daughter.

Perduta But . . . you see . . . I love it here . . . You're very kind, but . . . I don't really want to go.

The Contessa sits, shattered

Contessa Oh . . .

Perduta (*confused*) Oh . . . I mean . . . that sounds very unkind . . . I know you are my mother, and I'm sure I shall come to love you, and it must be wonderful to be rich . . . but I do love it so, being with all the musicians, and especially Maestra Silvia . . . Will there be music in your house?

Contessa There will be whatever you wish there to be. There is music in almost every street in Venice, and in Rome it is very grand, with the opera, and the great concerts in the palaces, and the oratorios and masses in the churches. We might employ one or two musicians to play for you, if that would be what you want.

Perduta Really! . . . I would have my own orchestra?

Contessa Not orchestra exactly. But some servants who would play, whenever you want them to.

Perduta That would be wonderful!

Contessa We must get to know each other, Perduta. We are strangers yet. It will take a little time, for both of us. My name is Livia.

Perduta I think I shall just call you Mother.

Contessa I would like that.

Perduta Will I have to go . . . I mean . . . will I come with you before the end of the Carnival?

Contessa Would you like to stay till then?

Perduta Yes please! I love Carnival best of all the year!

Contessa Then why not? We shall see a good deal of each other from now on.

Perduta (*not quite certain*) Yes . . .

Contessa Madre?

The Madre enters, and Sisters Teresa and Annunciata stand in the door

The Contessa speaks quietly to the Madre

I don't have the slightest doubt, Madre, now I've seen her. She's adorable, and I *know* she's mine. She is very uncertain at the moment, and I must get her used to the idea of changing her life slowly, and with great care. She wants to stay till the end of the Carnival, and I see no harm in that. I shall take her immediately after.

Madre There are some formalities to be completed with the Governors, but there is plenty of time. Are you happy now, Perduta, to have found your mother?

Perduta (*slightly unconvinced*) Yes Madre. Wonderfully happy.

Madre Take her back to her quarters now, Sister Teresa.

The Contessa crosses to Perduta, holds her lightly by the shoulders, and kisses her forehead. Perduta barely responds

Contessa Goodbye, my child: for the moment.

Perduta Goodbye, Mother.

Sister Teresa takes Perduta out

Contessa I can never thank you enough. To have lived the life I have lived, and then to be rewarded like this . . .

Madre Your pleasure is my reward, my lady.

Contessa Indeed, but it will take a more practical form. I intend to settle a very large sum on the Ospedale . . .

Madre That will be most generous.

Contessa And I shall not forget your part in this business . . .

Sister Annunciata is looking at the Madre almost with a grin

Madre No, my lady. I need nothing. What has passed between us is more important than money.

Contessa Is that what you mean by the truth of Heaven, Madre, rather than the truth of Venice?

Madre In my prayers, I most fervently hope it is. (*She bows her head*)

The Contessa leaves through the door opened for her by Sister Annunciata

When she has gone, Sister Annunciata looks at the Madre, almost with contempt, and follows the Contessa out

The Madre stands quite still

The scene changes to a street in Venice

Milord enters, dressed and masked as Arlecchino, followed by Bodger, dressed and masked as Scapino. The nose on Bodger's mask is very long

Bodger I feel a complete idiot done up like this!

Milord Enter into the spirit of the thing, Bodger. It's Carnival.

Bodger My own face is bad enough.

Milord Not at all, Bodger. It expresses a benign stupidity which I find most comforting.

Bodger Well this thing doesn't! (*Referring to his mask*) It makes me look like a cross between a drivelling cretin and a raving maniac.

Milord It's Scapino, Bodger, a merry prankful fellow who's always getting into all kinds of amusing japes.

Bodger Oh har har, how wonderfully funny! What about you?

Milord I am Arlecchino.

Bodger You look like something from a pack of cards. A full house in diamonds.

Milord Arlecchino is a melancholy clown, sad and beautiful, and a lover and a poet!

Bodger I'm glad I don't work for him then. He sounds a right turn-off.

Milord The point is, Bodger, we are in disguise, and so is everyone else. No-one knows who we are, and everything is possible!

Bodger While I've got this thing on, nothing is possible!

Pazzo and Grimaldo enter, Pazzo dressed and masked as Silenus, Grimaldo as the Devil. Pazzo pushes a barrow full of paintings, covered by a cloth

Pazzo Ah, signori!

Bodger Watch out sir, I don't like the look of these two!

Pazzo The English Milord and his man!

Bodger I thought we were supposed to be in disguise?

Pazzo Englishmen are recognizable everywhere, signori.

Milord Who are you then?

Grimaldo I am the Devil!

Pazzo And I am Silenus.

Bodger Si who?

Milord Remember your classical education, Bodger!

Bodger I didn't have one.

Milord He's a disgusting fat old drunk who seduces everybody.

Bodger Maybe I've been missing something.

Pazzo We welcome Arlecchino and Scapino to all the joys of Carnival! We are otherwise your good friends Pazzo, and the Count Grimaldo!

Grimaldo Infernally at your service, signori!

General laughter and delight. Milord looks at the barrow

Milord What's all this?

Pazzo This, signore, (*removing the cloth*) is a barrowload of Canalettos, specially for you!

Milord Really? That's wonderful!

Grimaldo The painter is a client of mine. One word from me, he paints a dozen of these.

Milord Oh look, Bodger, this is just the job! Hang these in the parlour and everyone will know where we've been! How can you bear to be parted from them?

Grimaldo Only with the greatest pain, signore.

Pazzo Or two guineas a picture. You won't do better anywhere in Venice. Half a guinea below the going rate.

Milord That seems an awful lot of money.

Pazzo All right then, signore, I won't argue. Twenty guineas the barrowload. I haven't even counted them, signore, I don't even know what's there, I'm probably losing a fortune. But for an English friend . . . !

Milord Twenty guineas a barrowload, that's really generous, isn't it, Bodger!

Bodger It's more than my year's wages!

Milord Yes, I'll take them!

Grimaldo Wine, signore, we have wine, of course.

Milord Of course!

Pazzo Anyone can drink old wine, signore, ten-year-old Barolos and Brunellos. Don't touch any of it, signore, that's all gone right out of fashion this year.

Milord Really?

Pazzo We can get you some of the very latest thing, like nectar of the gods, signore, what all the glittering people are drinking on the Grand Canal. Tuscan White! (*Pazzo produces a bottle and glass from within his costume*)

Milord And how old is that?

Pazzo Three months, signore. Young wine for the young at heart. Half a guinea for five gallons.

Pazzo pours a glass for Grimaldo, who goes through the full wine-tasting routine, eventually spitting the full mouthful on to Bodger's shoes. Then Pazzo pours a glass for Milord, who imitates everything Grimaldo has done, but drinks the wine, smiling knowingly as it rips the top off his tongue

Milord Oh, I say, that's a wonderful bargain. What do you think, Bodger?

Bodger I don't care how old it is, as long as it makes you drunk. (*Bodger takes a pull from the bottle, but has to spit it out almost at once*)

Milord Oh yes, we'll certainly have some of that. But there is one thing more I do want.

Grimaldo And what is that, signore? If it exists in the Empire of Hell, you shall have it!

Milord Music. I need lots and lots of music. I'm going to marry this wonderful girl, who is a musician, so I must have whole libraries of the stuff!

Grimaldo I have already made an appointment for you, signore, with Maestro Vivaldi. He will sell you anything.

Milord Oh, that's wonderful news! What a morning we're having, eh, Bodger?

Bodger A very expensive morning, sir.

Grimaldo And it's only just beginning! This is Carnival! Everywhere you go there is music in the air, passion in the heart, and seduction in the shadows. Venice is full of Columbines, waiting for their Arlecchinos!

Milord And I can't wait, can you, Bodger? Lead me to it!

Bodger Wait for me, sir. I won't get near enough to seduce anything, wearing this thing . . .

Bodger follows Milord off, still struggling with his mask

Pazzo Signore!

Grimaldo What?

Pazzo We can't take them to see Vivaldi. Or at least, not *our* Vivaldi! The real one's in town!

Grimaldo So what? We take them to see the real one.

Pazzo Are you sure? He's got a terrible temper, and he's even more rapacious about money than we are.

Grimaldo Then he will be more than pleased to meet two English idiots. I've seen Vivaldi sell the same set of concertos to ten different customers in a morning, and make each one of them believe he's written them exclusively for them!

Pazzo Then what do we get out of it?

Grimaldo Commission!

Pazzo and Grimaldo go off

Milord comes back, calling Bodger

Milord Bodger, you fool!

Bodger What?

Milord You've forgotten our barrowload of Canalettos!

They go off again, Bodger wheeling the barrowload

The scene changes, and the stage represents the interior of the Pietà during a working morning, being roughly divided into a central area, like a large meeting hall or common room, and an area DL which represents a study in which Vivaldi works — not much more than a table and a chair — and an area DR which is Silvia's private space, perhaps a small teaching or playing room reserved for members of the privilegiate. There is a kind of illuminated sheet or shadow wall behind which at times Silvia can be seen playing

All the members of the orchestra gather in the central area, with their instruments, talking, chatting, tuning up. Prudenza and her group gather downstage

Prudenza Listen, it's fixed for tonight!

Michelotta I don't believe you! How did you do it?

Prudenza Gave him money. My last teaching fee!

Paulina He's a filthy old crook, that back gateman.

Pellegrina How do you know he won't take the money, and then betray us to the Madre?

Prudenza Because I'm paying him a third when we go, and two thirds when we get back!

Paulina That's a clever idea.

Michelotta Who told you that?

Prudenza This is Venice, and everybody breathes finance instead of air. You just lift up your hands to the sky, and grab!

Paulina Handfuls of ways to make money!

Prudenza That's right. So all be ready at eight. We can even put our masks

in the gatehouse, while he's not looking.
Michelotta Isn't it exciting!
Prudenza I shall find my beautiful young man tonight. For sure!

The interest switches to the DR *area where Silvia is talking to Anna-Maria*

Silvia I'm going out to Carnival tonight. Are you coming?
Anna-Maria No, I don't think so.
Silvia You'll be just about the only one left inside I should think.
Anna-Maria No. Most of the girls are too frightened.
Silvia Are you?
Anna-Maria No. I don't feel in a Carnival mood.

Soprana and Anastazia join them, full of excitement

Soprana Maestra Silvia!
Anastazia Maestr'Anna!
Anna-Maria What?
Silvia Such excitement!
Soprana We've just been with Vandini!
Anastazia We're both to become soloists, when the Carnival is over!
Anna-Maria Ah, brava!
Silvia Straight into dead women's shoes, eh?
Anna-Maria That's wonderful news!
Anastazia So I shall be doing the principal violin solos, with Prudenza.
Silvia And you'll be doing my cello concertos?
Soprana Yes, I'm so excited and so frightened at the same time!
Silvia So you should be. No-one on earth can play them except me.
Anna-Maria Take no notice. Give you two years, you'll leave her far behind!
Silvia How old are you?
Soprana I'm seventeen. Anastazia's sixteen.
Silvia Well, make the most of it. I was fourteen when I started playing solos. How old were you, Anna?
Anna-Maria Fifteen.
Silvia It's a short life, but a glorious one!
Anastazia It's so thrilling!
Soprana I can't wait!
Silvia At least wait for us to be decently buried before you step into our shrouds.

Vandini has entered, and begins to address the girls, who, for a miracle, listen to him almost first time

Vandini My children . . . daughters of the Muse! . . . The rehearsals and teaching sessions will begin at once. The strings of the main orchestra will go to the Music Salon. The *Privilegiate* who are teaching will meet their pupils here, and the four *Initziate* must go with Perduta to the library, before joining the rehearsal later. We must play well today, my children, Maestro Vivaldi will be here to listen to us later. To your rehearsals and lessons now, daughters of the Muse, as quickly as you can!

The group begins to break up, going its different ways

The four Initziate gather round Perduta

Margarita Why do we have to go with you, Perduta? You're not a musician.

Chiaretta Shhh, Margarita . . .

Perduta There's more than one sort of musician, Margarita. You must come with me to the library.

Fortunata Why?

Perduta There is a great deal of sorting out of scores to be done. Before I go.

Giulietta Are you going, Perduta? Where?

Margarita Haven't you heard? Her mother's come back.

Fortunata I wish mine would come back.

Giulietta Is that true, Perduta?

Margarita I don't think I ever had one. I don't care anyway.

Perduta Yes, it is.

Chiaretta And are you really going?

Perduta Yes, I suppose so. I think I am.

Margarita Who will look after the library?

Perduta We don't know yet. That's why we must get everything fully sorted out. Come on.

Already we can hear distant sounds of musical rehearsal, the string section playing the same ritornello over and over again, solo oboes, flutes and bassoons practising, some with harpsichord, some not, and in the distance an a cappella choir

As the five young girls walk off-stage led by Perduta . . .

Vivaldi enters, carrying a large bundle of MS music, and goes to his little table DL where he begins writing on the music paper, with great speed and intensity, utterly oblivious of the sounds all round him

Silvia and Anna-Maria are still together DR

Silvia Why won't you come? Faithful to your Englishman already?

Anna-Maria No. I don't know what it is. I feel very strange about it all the time. Don't you?

Silvia No, not now it's all decided. It's exciting and dangerous, and I want to get out of here as soon as possible. It's all over here for us. The past, already.

Anna-Maria I wish I felt so sure.

Silvia You are going to marry your Milord, aren't you?

Anna-Maria Yes, I suppose so.

Silvia You'd be mad not to.

Anna-Maria Oh . . . here's my pupil. I'll see you later, after the lesson. (*She goes US to meet her pupil*)

Maestra Luciana and Lucietta enter obliquely at opposite sides, and can't help meeting

Lucietta Maestra Luciana . . .
Luciana Ah. Lucietta.
Lucietta I don't know what to say . . .
Luciana Then say nothing. Our next lesson is tomorrow morning, I believe. We must work very hard for the next month. There is a great deal to tell you, in a very short time.
Lucietta It wasn't my fault, Maestra. I shall never teach as well as you do, I haven't the experience . . .
Luciana Well. You'll soon learn.
Lucietta What shall I do, Maestra, without you to help me?
Luciana Become what you really are. A mature artist, who needs no-one. Just remember one thing, child.
Lucietta What?
Luciana When the time comes, they will throw you out with the rubbish too. Be ready for that day.
Lucietta I can't bear it, Maestra.
Luciana I have been prepared for it for some time. The young must always take the place of the old. It's the law of nature.
Lucietta What will you do, Maestra?
Luciana I don't know. I must find somewhere to live.

Luciana wanders off, in a kind of a daze. She has understood what has happened to her, and knows how she should react: and yet she is paralysed

Lucietta looks round for someone to talk to in her distress, sees Vivaldi at his desk writing, and tentatively goes towards him

Lucietta Maestro Vivaldi.
Vivaldi (*not looking up*) What is it, Maestra Lucietta? I have a flute concerto to finish by five o'clock.
Lucietta It's about Maestra Luciana, Maestro.
Vivaldi Yes. What about her?
Lucietta You know, they . . .
Vivaldi They've sacked her, yes. It happens to musicians all the time. It has happened to me here, twice, and will do again.
Lucietta But you are a great violinist, Maestro, and composer. She has nothing.
Vivaldi She is an artist.
Lucietta But where can she play, Maestro, except here?
Vivaldi Well. It isn't my business, Maestra. Or yours.
Lucietta No, Maestro.
Vivaldi It's a hard life, making music. My turn will come. So will yours.
Lucietta Yes, Maestro.
Vivaldi Now leave me please, Maestra. I am busy.
Lucietta Yes, Maestro . . .

Lucietta wanders uncertainly away from Vivaldi, who doesn't look up. Silvia calls across to her from her area

Silvia Lucietta, will you come and play through this sonata with me?
Lucietta Yes . . . I'll come . . .

Lucietta turns and sees Soprana and Anastazia crossing the stage with their instruments

Soprana, will you come and play the continuo?
Soprana But Maestra Lucietta, I'm supposed to be —
Lucietta Now, please.

Lucietta and Soprana join Silvia and all three go behind the lighted sheet. In shadow we see and hear them begin to play a movement of a cello sonata by Vivaldi, Lucietta accompanying Silvia on harpsichord, Soprana playing cello continuo

Anastazia goes off-stage

After a few moments of music, Perduta comes on stage. She listens to the music all around her, all kinds of sounds: but she gradually becomes aware of the dominant sound of Silvia playing the cello sonata. Tears are welling in her eyes as she moves across to Silvia's area. She hurriedly wipes them away as . . .

Candida enters

Candida What are you doing here?
Perduta Nothing, Maestra, . . . I . . .
Candida Who are you waiting for?
Perduta Nobody, Maestra, I'm listening to Maestra Silvia play.
Candida You're going out, I suppose, like all the others?
Perduta Out, Maestra?
Candida To the Carnival.
Perduta No, Maestra. It's forbidden.
Candida But everyone does it. I don't think there'll be a Maestra within doors tonight.
Perduta Except you, Maestra.
Candida Why do you say that?
Perduta I . . . I don't know . . .
Candida There's nothing out there. I shall play to please myself for a change. I can't imagine why everyone should be so keen to wear masks and make fools of themselves. Can you?
Perduta No, Maestra.
Candida Well. What would you know about it?
Perduta Nothing, Maestra.

Candida gives her a contemptuous look, and sweeps out

Almost at the same time, the cello playing stops, and Maestra Silvia comes on stage, carrying her cello, looking for a piece of music she has mislaid. Perduta calls tentatively

Perduta Maestra Silvia . . . ?

Silvia What is it, I'm in the middle of playing. Did I send for you?

Perduta No, Maestra.

Silvia What do you want then?

Perduta Can I speak with you, Maestra, for a minute?

Silvia Now?

Perduta Yes please, Maestra, if you would.

Silvia Just a moment, Lucietta . . . What is it?

Perduta You've heard . . . of my good fortune, Maestra?

Silvia Oh yes. Our little Contessa. Well. You're lucky. We all had parents
once upon a time. Even me. But most of us never find them. So. Make
the most of your good luck.

Perduta Maestra, I wanted . . .

Silvia What?

Perduta I've always admired you, Maestra Silvia, more than all the others.
I can't move when you play. It's like a magic spell.

Silvia Well, that's charming of you, little Contessa. Now . . .

Perduta And I wondered . . .

Silvia What?

Perduta My mother . . . my new mother, told me that . . .

Silvia What?

Perduta That I could have my own little orchestra, when I leave here. In
her palace. Three or four maybe, who could play with me . . .

Silvia Yes? And?

Perduta I know you have to go, Maestra, and I wondered . . . Will you
come with us?

Silvia What?

Perduta I know how difficult it is when our great musicians have to
leave. And you are the greatest of all. My mother would pay you. You
would live with us in our palace. And then you wouldn't have to . . .
have to . . .

Silvia I don't know whether my ears are going wrong or I've gone mad.
You are suggesting that I become your mother's . . . musical servant?

Perduta No, Maestra, not like that! I just thought you had nowhere to go,
and . . .

Silvia Well, I have somewhere to go, thank you very much, and it isn't into
anyone's house to be a servant. Even a cello servant! Now. Was there
anything else?

Perduta No. I'm sorry, Maestra.

Silvia It was kind of you, little Contessa. But you know nothing of what
goes on. You are too young to understand.

Perduta I don't want to go at all. Not without you! I'd much rather stay
here and work in the library. I'd hate to be all on my own there, while
all the rest of you stay here.

Silvia I won't be here.

Perduta Where are you going, Maestra?

Silvia Never you mind. Now listen, silly little bitch. You are one of the lucky ones. Grab that Contessa of yours, grab her with both hands and never let go. Because she will make a life for you, and you will never have a life here. Do you understand?

Perduta Yes, Maestra.

Silvia There have been plenty of girls who have had crushes on me before now. I had them myself at your age. And where are those girls I worshipped so much now? God knows. If you admire me so much, do what I tell you. Hang on to that mother. And get out of here.

Perduta Yes, Maestra . . .

Silvia Now go. You are disturbing my playing.

Perduta Yes, Maestra . . . *(She goes into the central area)*

Behind the sheet, Silvia picks up the cello sonata where she left it

Perduta listens for a moment. Then, her face crumpled with pain, she exits

The music continues as Anna-Maria comes from the back, her lesson over, towards Silvia's area

Vivaldi looks up, and sees her

Vivaldi Maestr'Anna?

Anna-Maria Maestro? *(She goes across to him)*

Vivaldi There will be a new concerto for you to play before the end of Carnival. I wrote it for you last night. The little copyist will have it ready in a few days.

Anna-Maria Thank you, Maestro.

Vivaldi You played my seasonal concertos as well as I've ever heard them. You are a great artist. I kiss your feet.

Anna-Maria I am honoured, Maestro.

Vivaldi It is a tragedy you must stop playing. But that is how the world is for women. And we men can give thanks to God for the chance of earning our bread a little longer.

Anna-Maria Yes, Maestro . . . I . . .

Vivaldi You are not going to the nunnery are you? I heard you were getting married.

Anna-Maria Yes . . . I suppose I am.

Vivaldi An Englishman.

Anna-Maria Yes.

Vivaldi Good. Marry him. They will adore you in England. I have never been to London, but there is some music there. You will be able to play in private at least, if your husband will allow it. The orchestras there are not as good, but then, nowhere is the equal of the Pietà.

Anna-Maria Maestro, I wondered . . . ?

Vivaldi What?

Anna-Maria I know a woman cannot live as an orchestral player. But I can sing too. Many people have praised my singing. Do you think it might be possible . . . ?

Vivaldi Have you ever sung in opera, on a public stage?

Anna-Maria No . . .
Vivaldi It is very different from singing solos in church, I assure you. I have
never heard you sing. You were not singing before I went away.
Anna-Maria No, Maestro, but I sing the principal soprano parts now.
Vivaldi As well as the violin. Well. Good. But that is not uncommon in
the Pietà.
Anna-Maria I wondered . . . if I might live as a singer?
Vivaldi What, you?
Anna-Maria Yes sir.
Vivaldi No. No. Not the slightest chance. Put it out of your head. Marry
your Englishman and breed children.
Anna-Maria But Maestro . . .
Vivaldi Take any possibility of happiness when it is offered. Seize it! Only
a fool chooses pain. An artist's life is much anguish and little pleasure.
Sometimes none. Play my new concerto. Get married, and go . . .
Anna-Maria Thank you Maestro . . .
Vivaldi I will go through the solo part with you when it is copied.
Anna-Maria Yes Maestro . . .

*Anna-Maria goes to the centre of the stage, and looks round at the
echoing sounds of practice. Silvia's cello sonata is finished. Suddenly
Anna-Maria calls*

Silvia!
Silvia (*entering from behind the sheet*) Yes?
Anna-Maria Are you going to the Carnival tonight?
Silvia Yes.
Anna-Maria I'm coming with you.

They go off

*A huge burst of joyful music as they go, and the scene changes to a square
in Venice, overlooking the water. It is early evening*

*The stage fills with people, all masked, mostly wearing anonymous
tricorne, white mask, black bauta and long cloak, but about half in
exotic and outrageous fancy dress of all kinds. There is a continuous
sound of music, some being played in the street, some coming from
concerts or balls within doors, where the windows stand open and
the sound and light streams out. Most of the street music is dance
music, or popular songs, bawled in a whole gamut of untrained and
semi-sober voices, and accompanied by jigging people in various stages
of intoxication and merriment. There are tumblers, performing to pipe
and tabor, a group of laughing people heading towards some kind of
lighted gathering, a drunk or two. Two masked men drift on, following the
same masked woman, who leads them on, almost as if all three were in a
trance. There are thieves, pickpockets, dancers, actors, pimps, courtesans
with their train of little black servants, and a group of people carrying
coloured lanterns on long poles, as well as waiters carrying flasks and
jugs of wine*

Through the swirl of action, a slim and elegant young man moves slowly, looking round him. He wears the conventional bone-white mask, with tricorne and cloak, and looks both beautiful and a little sinister

Bodger enters, followed by Milord. Milord is still dressed as Arlecchino, but Bodger has discarded his Scapino mask, in favour of a red devil mask, which he wears with the conventional tricorne and cloak, over his Scapino costume

Bodger Now this is more like it!

Milord There are dozens of red devils, Bodger! I shan't be able to tell which one is you and which isn't. What have you done with your Scapino mask?

Bodger Threw it in the canal and watched it sink. It went nose-last like a ship's rigging!

Milord I think it's a shame. We made a good pair.

Bodger With that great pointed conk on me, sir, I might have been able to pin a girl to the wall, but I wouldn't have stood a chance of kissing her.

Some early evening fireworks go off, in a great burst of colour, and most of the Carnival revellers turn to watch them. The beautiful young man is studying Bodger with interest

Milord Well, this is it, Bodger! Isn't it exciting!

Bodger Well no, not at this very moment it isn't. But it has possibilities.

Two masked Columbines enter, drifting provocatively

Milord Here we are, Bodger! Action stations!

Bodger What?

Milord Prepare a boarding party!

Two brawny Arlecchinos follow, being led on by the Columbines

The two Columbines curtsy to Milord and Bodger, who raise their hats in a rather stiff English fashion. The two Arlecchinos bow deeply as they pass Milord and Bodger, and then, just before their exit, do a sudden threatening step towards Milord and Bodger, which nearly makes them jump out of their skins

The two Arlecchinos go off laughing, after the Columbines

Milord I think they had the wind of us there, Bodger.

Bodger I think we sank with all hands, sir.

The Young Man calls to Bodger from the shadows

Young Man Red Devil!

Bodger (*looking round*) What?

Young Man Red Devil! Over here . . .

Bodger Look!

Milord What?
Bodger I'm being propositioned!
Milord I say!
Bodger Can't see what she looks like in those shadows.
Milord Worth coming to Venice, eh Bodger?
Bodger Well, you certainly don't get anything like this in Leicester!
Young Man Come on, Red Devil. Don't be afraid.

Giggles and signs between Milord and Bodger

Bodger (*to the Young Man*) Don't be misled by the mask. There's more to me than meets the eye.
Young Man Is it a mask? I took you to be devil through and through.
Bodger You could be right! (*He is now close to the Young Man, still half in the shadow*)
Young Man Your voice is darker toned than I expected. (*He moves out into the light a little*)
Bodger So is yours . . . Eh? Wait a minute. You're wearing trousers!
Young Man So are you!
Bodger What do you think I am?
Young Man Not my kind of devil.
Bodger Not mine either! Go to Hell.
Young Man Not with you, Beelzebub!
Bodger No . . . well . . . I mean . . .

The Young Man has slithered into the darkness

Bodger wanders back to Milord

Milord Well, Bodger? Where's she gone?
Bodger That's a good question.
Milord What were you up to over there?
Bodger So's that.

A laughing procession of people with lamps crosses the stage

Bodger Why don't we join on? Can't do any worse.
Milord Why not? Let us exploit the freedom of anonymity to the uttermost.
Bodger You can do what you like. I'm just going to make the most of being disguised.

They go off together

Two of the masked people of the procession have remained on stage, a lady with a white mask, white tricorne and a white cloak, and a man in a full Mr Punch fancy dress and mask, hump and all, the woman seeming pure and ethereal, the man ugly and grotesque. The woman in white is Candida, though at no point in the scene do we see her face, and Mr Punch is, of course, the Punch and Judy Man

Mr Punch I've been watching you, Lady in White.

Candida Have you Mr Punch?
Mr Punch You're on your own. You've got nowhere to go.
Candida I can go home.
Mr Punch No-one goes home during Carnival.
Candida Not you, Mr Punch?
Mr Punch Not without Judy. She went. It's hard running the show on my own.
Candida The show? Where?
Mr Punch In the street. Under the colonnade. In the square. In the convent. Wherever people will pay to see Punch beat Judy.
Candida Is that all he does?
Mr Punch Every time. Makes people laugh.
Candida It must be good to make people laugh.
Mr Punch It's a living. Can you make a puppet?
Candida No.
Mr Punch Or make it dance?
Candida No.
Mr Punch What can you do?
Candida I can sing.
Mr Punch I've never seen a Judy who can sing. Even funnier if he beats her when she's singing.
Candida Yes. Much funnier.
Mr Punch Come and sing for me.
Candida Where?
Mr Punch In the street. Under the colonnade. In the square. Not in the convent though.
Candida No. Not in the convent.

They go off together

After a few seconds Pazzo and Grimaldo enter, still costumed as the Devil and Silenus

Grimaldo Pazzo, the birds have flown! Venice is full of Arlecchinos and Scapinos! There must be a thousand of them.
Pazzo We won't miss them. Englishmen walk differently.
Grimaldo What, not one foot in front of the other?
Pazzo No, signore, you know what I mean! Italians prance, Spaniards lurk, Frenchmen mince . . .
Grimaldo Germans stagger. What do Englishmen do?
Pazzo They plod, signore. Like oxen. Big and dumb.
Grimaldo You cut their hide off in strips, to make boot-leather!
Pazzo That's right, signore.
Grimaldo We must find them, Pazzo. All that money!
Pazzo It's painful to think of it still in his pockets, and not in ours!
Grimaldo And Maestro Vivaldi himself, waiting to swindle them in his lodgings!
Pazzo We will, signore. Remember! Watch for the walk!

They hurry off together

*The Young Man enters, and lurks behind a pillar. Music plays. Masked,
cloaked and full-skirted figures come and go in the half-dark*

*Prudenza enters, followed by Pellegrina, Paulina and Michelotta. The
latter three are costumed and masked as nymphs or dryads. Prudenza
has the same sort of costume, but with an incongruous Red Devil mask
at the top*

Pellegrina I don't know how you dare, Prudenza! Everyone's staring!
Prudenza That's the idea.
Paulina It's very disturbing. A nymph with the face of a devil.
Prudenza No more than anyone else . . .
Michelotta Of course it is. It's grotesque!
Prudenza The disturbing thing is how many look like nymphs with their
masks on, and are devils underneath!
Pellegrina Everyone looks the same in the cloaks and the white masks.
Those are the real disguises.
Michelotta The ones who really want to be anonymous.
Pellegrina Aristocrats, churchmen, beggars!
Paulina It could be anybody. Old men, or women even, or the most
handsome young men!
Prudenza That's the point.
Michelotta But those three who followed us, they were young, I'm sure,
and very handsome!
Pellegrina Why didn't you go with them then?
Michelotta Oh, I was much too frightened!
Pellegrina As long as we stick together we'll be safe.
Paulina Prudenza . . .
Prudenza What?
Paulina That young man, in the shadows. He's looking at you.
Prudenza Where?
Paulina There.
Prudenza It's him!
Michelotta It can't be.
Pellegrina Are you sure?
Paulina How can you tell?
Prudenza I'd recognize those gorgeous legs anywhere!

They laugh and giggle

Pellegrina What are you going to do?
Prudenza See if he makes a move.
Young Man Red Devil!
Michelotta It is him, it must be!
Pellegrina Shhhh . . .
Michelotta Be careful . . .
Young Man Red Devil. Don't be afraid.
Prudenza I'm not afraid.
Young Man Come here. I'm sure you're the devil I've been looking for.

Prudenza goes a little way towards him, then stops

Prudenza So am I.
Young Man I've been watching you for weeks. Every day.
Prudenza By the pillar at the Cardinal's. And in church.
Young Man I can't take my eyes off you.
Pellegrina Oh God, isn't this exciting!
Michelotta Scary!
Paulina Shhh!
Prudenza I sent you a note . . .
Young Man Then why are we waiting. Come here.

Slowly, deliberately, Prudenza crosses to him

Your hand, Madonna.
Prudenza My hand . . . ?
Young Man To kiss. Why else did we meet? In the shadows. And masked.

Nervously she holds out her hand. The Young Man caresses it in his own, then kisses it

Prudenza Oh . . . Your hand is very slender and white.
Young Man Not as slender as yours, Madonna.
Prudenza And your voice is very soft and gentle. Do you sing?
Young Man Alas, no.
Prudenza You should.
Young Man I have no art for it. I simply admire those who have. Like you, Madonna.
Prudenza Can I see your face?
Young Man What do faces matter? This is Carnival. We should keep our masks on all night.
Prudenza I've only seen you from a distance.
Young Man You'll get a surprise.
Prudenza I want to see if you are as beautiful close up as you are far away.
Young Man Oh yes . . . yes . . . *(He takes off the mask)*
Prudenza Oh . . .
Young Man Well? Am I?
Prudenza But . . . you're a girl.
Young Man *(grasping her arm)* Of course I am. You knew that all along, Madonna, surely!
Prudenza *(retreating)* No . . . I didn't . . . no!
Young Man Don't run away!
Prudenza No, no . . . I can't . . .

The Young Man releases his grip, and Prudenza runs back to the other girls, who have been watching awestruck, but have not seen the denouement

Pellegrina What is it, what's the matter . . . ?
Prudenza Let's go, quickly, let's go . . .
Michelotta Why, what happened?
Prudenza Let's go!

She hustles the other girls off stage

The Young Man has slowly re-assumed his mask. He looks round, and slides silently into the darkness

The scene changes to the Madre's room in the Pietà, early evening, beginning to get dark

The Madre is already on-stage with Sister Annunciata

Sister Teresa enters from the ante room

Sister Teresa She's still in tears, Madre. She says she won't go.
Madre She must go. She has no choice in the matter.
Sister Annunciata We can't force her, Madre.
Madre Of course we can. She lives on the charity of the Pietà. We can give her to whom we please.
Sister Teresa But we never turn children out on to the street . . .
Sister Annunciata We have no right to force her, Madre. The woman is not her mother. We might just as well sell her to a Turkish dealer for a brothel.
Madre Be calm, Sister. She is a child, and hysterical with emotion. We know what is best for her.
Sister Annunciata Do we? Or is it best for us?
Madre For the Pietà, and for her.
Sister Annunciata We are telling a lie.
Sister Teresa If the child still refuses to go, Madre, the mother will insist that she has the right to take her. And she has not.
Sister Annunciata Then someone will have to look at the records, and the truth will come out. If that happens she will kill you.
Madre It won't happen, Sister. We shall see to that.
Sister Annunciata How?
Madre Persuade the child. Or falsify the record.
Sister Annunciata Madre!
Madre The responsibility is mine, Sister. And you, let me remind you both, are commanded to silence. Bring the child in.
Sister Teresa Yes Madre.

Sister Teresa goes

Madre And leave us alone.

Sister Annunciata goes

After a few moments Perduta enters, looking pale, bedraggled and wet-eyed

The Madre sits her down

Now, my little copyist. You look most unhappy.
Perduta Don't send me away, Madre. I love it here so much. All my friends. And the music.
Madre I know how much you love it, Perduta, life is full of things we

love. You will learn as you get older that the story of our days is how, gradually, one by one, we lose them.

Perduta But why should I lose them yet, Madre?

Madre You will have to go soon. In seven years.

Perduta That's more than half my life, Madre.

Madre You will never get a better chance than the great joy of finding your own mother, who wants you, and will love you.

Perduta She doesn't feel like my mother at all. She is very grand, and she frightens me.

Madre That is because you have been brought up in a convent, and know nothing of the world. She is a fine lady, intelligent, and for her sort, kind. She has a great need of you, and will love you very much: just as a mother should.

Perduta But, Madre —

Madre Do not miss the chance, child. It comes only once in life, and if you miss it, it is gone for good. Venice is full of gondolas. Imagine if you were all alone on the island of tombs, and only one gondola could take you off. If you missed it, you would have to stay there alone, among the dead, for ever.

Perduta I'm not alone here, Madre.

Madre, without making a fuss of it, makes sure the door is fully closed and no-one is listening

Madre Let me tell you . . . something an old and very wise nun told me. A sad story.

Perduta What, Madre?

Madre She was full of the love of Christ, even when she was girl. She had always wanted to be a nun. But when she was fifteen, just as she was about to take her vows, she fell in love. She conducted a secret affair with her lover for two years. And was very, very happy.

Perduta What happened?

Madre She found out that she was to have a child. And her lover deserted her.

Perduta That was horrible of him!

Madre And her parents too: they threw her out in the street. She was in despair. But she had the child. All alone. It was a time of terrible anguish. And . . .

Perduta Madre . . . ?

Madre She had it only a very short time. A few weeks. She couldn't manage on her own. She drowned her child, in the canal.

Perduta Oh . . .

Madre And then she tried to drown herself. But she was saved. And brought here.

Perduta Here, Madre? Was it here?

Madre Yes . . . the old nun . . . The nuns saved her life, and she took her vows and became a sister of the order. But for the rest of her life . . . her whole life . . .

Perduta What?

Madre She regretted that she had . . . thrown away the one person who would have loved her, the way children love their parents, and their parents love them. She would have had that. And she threw it away. Don't throw it away, Perduta. If you do, it is gone for ever.

Perduta When did she die, Madre? Was I here?

Madre Oh no. She died a long time ago. You do understand me, don't you. You have your life here at the moment, but it will pass, your friends will go and eventually you will have to go too. But where? To the nunnery yourself? Or the island of tombs?

Perduta Oh no. I don't think so. I don't feel at all like a nun.

Madre You don't understand what it is like to be rich. With money you can do what you like. When you are grown up and your own mistress, you can make your own orchestra, commission music from famous composers, even put on an opera. Money is power. It can enable you to shape your life exactly as you want to shape it.

Perduta Can I really? I hadn't thought of that.

Madre When do you see your mother again?

Perduta Tomorrow. Here.

Madre Take her in your arms and kiss her. Tell her how much you love her for finding you. Even if it's not true now, it will be.

Perduta Thank you, Madre.

Madre Do I have your promise?

Perduta Yes, Madre. I promise I will try . . . I do like the idea of commissioning an opera!

Madre Yes. I thought that might appeal to you. Sister Teresa!

Sister Teresa comes in

Sister Teresa Yes, Madre?

Madre Perduta is going back to the library.

Sister Teresa Yes, Madre.

Sister Annunciata comes in as Sister Teresa takes Perduta out. She looks after her, then back to the Madre

Sister Annunciata Have you persuaded her?

Madre I think so.

Sister Annunciata How did you do it?

Madre Bribery, Sister Annunciata. What other way is there?

The scene changes to the Carnival square in Venice as before, but later at night

Cloaked and masked figures drift languorously and provocatively in the semi-darkness. A lantern on the end of a pole swings slowly and sadly across the stage, the dark figure carrying it almost invisible. Melancholy music is heard

Anna-Maria enters as Columbine, and Silvia, dressed as a baroque version of the goddess Diana, the costume, boots and mask entirely of gold. Anna-Maria walks sadly across the stage, and looks out over the Lagoon.

Silvia watches her

Silvia   Oh, Columbine, Columbine,
                       The wood dove mourns,
                       Singing her sad song
                       Among the thorns.

Anna-Maria What's that?

Silvia I don't know. A fragment of something. Floated into my head.

Anna-Maria Me, you mean.

Silvia Well, you're not exactly a Carnival companion, are you.

Anna-Maria It's sad.

Silvia We've been to two balls, but you didn't want to dance.

Anna-Maria The music was dreadful.

Silvia And then we found a beautiful gathering, on a terrace overlooking
the Lagoon, with Chinese lanterns like beautiful red and gold moons
hanging from the trees, full of men and women who looked so elegantly
expensive, they might have been at a drinks party for the gods on
Olympus. But Columbine was silent. She didn't want to talk to anyone.

Anna-Maria There was nothing to say.

Silvia It isn't at all sad. It's Carnival. Everyone's enjoying themselves.

Anna-Maria Trying to . . . All desperately running to and fro behind their
masks, looking for something . . . they don't know what. Fun, or drink,
or laughter, or love. Sweat on their faces, if we could see them. Fear.
Despair.

Silvia So what are you looking for behind yours?

Anna-Maria I don't know either.

Silvia There are two sorts of people, Anna. The vast majority want as
much pleasure out of life — and that means money, food, wine,
singing, dancing and love-making, in varying proportions — as they
can cram into a single lifetime. That's all. Nothing else. Sensuality
and greed. Never a single thought crosses their minds that isn't in
pursuit of one of those ends. And Carnival is their great festival. The
celebration before the abstinence of Lent. I have great sympathy with
those people. I serve them. The others, in a very small minority, are
like you.

Anna-Maria And what do we want?

Silvia You must tell me that.

Anna-Maria To know . . . somehow. To understand all the joy and pain,
and then . . . somehow . . . to express it . . . Music.

Silvia Not me. Not tonight. Maybe never again.

Anna-Maria What do you want tonight then?

Silvia Some laughter. A drink. A little elegant flirtation. Nothing serious.

Anna-Maria Is that why you're the Goddess Diana, all in gold?

Silvia That's right. Not only am I very chaste, I am very expensive. Come
on. Let's find ourselves a few gods and heroes. Or failing that, a couple
of Venetians!

Silvia leads Anna-Maria off-stage

Pazzo enters carrying Milord over his shoulder, followed by Grimaldo, with Bodger lurking warily in the shadows. They are all still in their Carnival costumes, but Milord is bellowing with pain and holding his head. Pazzo flops him down in a café chair

Pazzo Signore, I apologize!

Milord Apologize! I'm not going near him again. You call him a composer? I call him a homicidal maniac!

Grimaldo It is possible to be both.

Milord He broke a violin over my head!

Pazzo It was a very old violin.

Grimaldo He had no further use for it.

Milord Old or not, he nearly cracked my head open! Bodger, where's Bodger?

Bodger Here I am, sir . . .

Milord Where have you been?

Bodger I ran downstairs when the trouble started, sir.

Milord What did I do? I mean, what did I say?

Pazzo Nothing, signore, nothing at all.

Milord I merely told the fellow I wanted to buy some of his music, and he sold me a set of brand new concertos he had only written the night before. Twenty guineas I paid.

Grimaldo *(aside)* That's two he owes us.

Milord What were they called, Bodger . . . ?

Bodger I don't know sir. "La" something.

Milord *"La Stravaganza"*. That's right!

Pazzo *(aside)* Published ten years ago. Buy them in any shop.

Milord Then he said was I going to play them myself, and I said yes, and he said in that case, he would have to give me lessons, and he would give me one every afternoon for a month, and it would cost me a guinea a time.

Pazzo A great honour, signore!

Milord I said wasn't that rather a lot, and he said his concertos were difficult, and I would need his help.

Bodger That's when I got out, sir. I've heard you play the violin, and I knew what was coming.

Milord He picked up some of the music, gave me a violin, and said "Play that." So I said, "What's the tune?" I mean, I don't read music that well, so . . .

Pazzo Ah sir! That was your error.

Grimaldo You should never play for Vivaldi unless you are a master. He has the true *furore del maestro*.

Pazzo The fire of genius, signore!

Bodger And he gets impatient with idiots too.

Milord He scowled at me, his eyes nearly popped out of his head, he wheezed like the old organ in our chapel, and staggered about looking for his stick . . .

Grimaldo Asthma, poor man!

Pazzo Gasping for air.

Milord Gasping, my foot! His face was as red as a beetroot, and he looked furious as twenty thousand devils!

Bodger I know what's coming.

Milord So I said, "I can play good old *Sir Roger*."

Bodger Oh no sir, you didn't, not good old *"Sir Roger"*!

Milord And he shouted "What!" So I started to play. And he howled, and roared, and screamed, and ran round the room covering his ears, and coughed and choked. And then he started beating me with his stick!

Grimaldo Perhaps he didn't like your tone, signore?

Pazzo Or your bowing technique?

Milord Then, still howling like something from the pit of Hell, he broke the violin over my head, yelled "How dare you waste my time, you musical assassin, you murderer of art!" And kicked me downstairs. He literally kicked me downstairs! He put his toe in my bum and pushed!

Pazzo Are you all right, sir?

Grimaldo Are you injured?

Pazzo Is all your money safe?

Milord What's more, he kept the twenty guineas. And he didn't give me the concertos! So I have been assaulted by a maniac, belaboured black and blue, robbed, and I still need music!

Pazzo Signore, we will take it upon ourselves to get you some music.

Milord As long as you don't introduce me to any more composers.

Bodger (*proffering a flask of wine*) Here sir, have a drink.

Milord Oh Bodger! Like an oasis in the desert!

Bodger Tastes all the better sir, when you've pinched it.

Pazzo leads Grimaldo downstage

Grimaldo Where can we get music, Pazzo?

Pazzo Name a place that's full of music, signore. Been playing the stuff for two hundred years, and never thrown any of it away?

Grimaldo The Pietà, Pazzo.

Pazzo And who lives in the Pietà?

Grimaldo Orphan girls, Pazzo. And nuns.

Pazzo And who gets in and out of the Pietà without any trouble at all?

Grimaldo Nuns again.

Pazzo So what should we be if we went to go in and out of the Pietà, signore?

Grimaldo Still nuns, Pazzo.

Pazzo Come on, Sister!

They hurry off chuckling

Silvia and Anna-Maria enter on the opposite side of the stage from Milord and Bodger

Milord Oh, that's better, Bodger.
Bodger Hey, look over there, sir!
Milord Where? By George, yes!
Bodger I think we're in luck, sir!
Milord Can't see any hulking Arlecchinos in the shadows, Bodger, waiting to pounce?
Bodger Don't think so, sir. Which is yours?
Milord Oh, Columbine, of course.
Bodger I'll take the gold one.
Milord Be careful, Bodger. All that glisters.
Bodger Doesn't worry me, sir. The cheaper the better, as far as I'm concerned.

Milord moves across to Anna-Maria, all elegance and poetry, while Bodger approaches Silvia in a somewhat more prosaic mood

Milord My Lady Columbine! Arlecchino presents his services.
Anna-Maria Oh . . . Columbine thanks Arlecchino for his courtesy.
Milord We belong together, my lady, on Carnival night.
Anna-Maria I believe we do . . .

He leads her to one side of the stage. On the other, Bodger is approaching Silvia

Bodger Goddess, I lay myself at your feet.
Silvia What can a goddess have to do with a devil? Particularly a Goddess of Chastity?
Bodger God knows, madam. But give me a minute, and I'll think of something. (*Bodger still has the bottle, and pours drinks for the two of them at a nearby table*)
Milord Are you sad, my Lady Columbine?
Anna-Maria Columbine is always sad.
Milord So is Arlecchino. He is a sad poet, full of love.
Anna-Maria Who are you in love with, Arlecchino?
Milord My Lady Columbine, madam. Who are you in love with?
Anna-Maria No-one. That's why I'm sad.
Milord Everyone should be happy at Carnival, Lady Columbine. For two months we cast off the cares of the real, and live behind a mask of pleasure.
Anna-Maria It's strange . . . wearing masks. It makes it possible to say things people wouldn't dare to say to each other face to face.
Milord And to share joys forbidden to all but masked creatures.

Bodger is now seated at a table with Silvia

Bodger Of course. I don't know who you are behind there. You could be a princess.
Silvia Or a whore.
Bodger Or both. That's the excitement.
Silvia And you could be . . . what?

Bodger Guess.

Silvia A coal heaver. A coachman. A brewer's drudge.

Bodger Oh, thanks a lot! How do you know I'm not a prince? Or a cardinal, come to that?

Silvia No. You're not a cardinal.

Anna-Maria I'm sad because a foolish man is in love with me: and I am not in love with him. But I have nowhere to go, and must share my life with him, or die.

Milord Why should you die, Columbine? There are other men. I am at your service.

Anna-Maria Because Orpheus, the God of Music, is my true love. But he doesn't return my devotion. And I am no longer allowed to be one of his servants.

Bodger Will you come with me, Goddess? Shall we find a quiet corner of Hell somewhere and play infernal games?

Silvia Or we could go to the pastures of Cithaeron, and you could worship my chastity.

Bodger My idea sounds more fun.

Milord scuttles across to the centre, and gestures Bodger to him

Milord Hey, Bodger, isn't this tremendous! I love this play-acting form of love-making!

Bodger It's OK, sir. But I wouldn't mind a bit of the real thing.

They giggle, whisper, and scuttle back to their respective ladies

Milord Then Arlecchino is much happier than Columbine. He has fallen in love since he came to Venice.

Anna-Maria With a goddess, or a woman?

Milord Oh a goddess, definitely! She plays the violin like a goddess. To speak plainly for a moment, she is the star violinist at the Pietà.

Anna-Maria turns to look at him, in horrified realization

She is an angel, and, what's more, she worships me! It's a good thing we're wearing masks, isn't it. I couldn't tell you any of this otherwise.

Anna-Maria Tell me more.

Milord It's paradise! And I'm taking her back to England with me! The only trouble is, I have a wife there, a pretty fearsome creature, and I must either get rid of her somehow, or keep this lovely Venetian goddess as my mistress. Which could be a very good thing to do, all things considered. One doesn't want such an unearthly creature as one's wife, after all. Not in England, at any rate.

Anna-Maria No?

Milord Not really. She's a kind of fantasy. And England is a horribly real place. Especially Leicestershire.

Anna-Maria Arlecchino.

Milord Yes, my Lady Columbine?

Anna-Maria We have shared our thoughts so completely, it's time we unmasked.

68   Daughters of Venice

Milord Gosh, is it really! How exciting!
Anna-Maria There is nothing further but to see each others faces.
Milord Then what shall we do? Go somewhere together?
Anna-Maria That depends.
Milord Do we always unmask at this point of the evening? I haven't been
  to Carnival before.
Anna-Maria Always.
Milord One after the other? Or at once?
Anna-Maria Both together. Are you ready?
Milord Yes.

*They both take their masks off. Milord doesn't realize for a second, then is
dumbstruck. Anna-Maria is in tears*

Anna-Maria There . . . Do you see now why Columbine is so sad?
Milord Oh my God, Bodger, I've bogged it! It's Anna-Maria!
Anna-Maria (*anguished*) Silvia!
Silvia What?
Anna-Maria Let's go, . . . quickly!

She gives a howl of pain, and hurries off, followed by Silvia

Silvia (*going*) Anna . . .
Bodger What's up, sir? I was just getting somewhere with Goldilocks.
Milord I've boshed it, Bodger, totally and utterly, put my foot in it right
  up to my bum!
Bodger Oh well, we can start again, sir. The night, as they say, is young!
Milord Oh no, Bodger, no! I've had quite enough play-acting for one
  evening! I'll tell you what though.
Bodger What?
Milord I wouldn't mind getting drunk instead!
Bodger Well, if the choice is between booze and women sir, at least you
  know where you are with booze.

They go off together

*The scene changes to the library of the Pietà, with plenty of old books of
music in evidence, leather-bound and dusty, and loose MS sheets*

*Perduta and the four Initziate are working away by lamplight, tired and fed
up, though Perduta's enthusiasm never flags*

Margarita How much longer, Perduta? I'm tired.
Perduta No-one goes to bed during Carnival. We shall see the dawn.
Fortunata Not in here we won't.
Giulietta No-one works during Carnival either.
Chiaretta Except us.
Margarita I think it's absolutely horrible to make us stay in sorting music
  while everyone else is outside enjoying themselves.
Perduta No-one's outside. It's not allowed. They're all in bed.
Margarita That's what you think. If I were to tell you everyone I know
  who's out tonight . . .

Perduta I wouldn't want to know.

Fortunata It's so boring. Nothing ever happens to us. All we do is sort out old dusty music that no-one ever plays any more.

Pazzo and Grimaldo enter, disguised, not very convincingly, as nuns of the Pietà

Grimaldo Good-evening, my children.

Perduta Good-evening, Sisters.

Grimaldo (*aside*) You didn't tell me all these would be here?

Pazzo (*aside*) I didn't know they would at this time of night, did I!

Grimaldo (*aside*) We'll never get away with it.

Pazzo (*aside*) We've got no choice now we're in! . . . Leave it to me . . .

Margarita Who are they?

Perduta I don't know.

Chiaretta Neither do I.

Pazzo Dear children, Sister Benedicta and I will take over now. You may go to your beds.

Perduta I don't think I know you, Sister. Who are you?

Pazzo I'm Sister Misericordia.

Grimaldo And I'm Sister Beata.

Pazzo (*aside*) No you're not, you're Sister Benedicta, I've just said so! Get it right!

Grimaldo (*aside*) Sorry . . . Benedicta, I mean. We've just come for a couple of armfuls of music, and we'll be off.

Giulietta That one's wearing boots!

Margarita What?

Giulietta Look, under her habit!

Chiaretta And their voices are very low.

Grimaldo Off you go to your beds, little cherubs. Sister Miserabilia and I will say a prayer for you.

Pazzo (*aside*) Misericordia, not Miserabilia!

Chiaretta And look at the hairs growing out of that one's ears!

Fortunata You've seen nuns with whiskers before.

Margarita Yes, but not nuns who shave every day.

Chiaretta They're men, aren't they!

Giulietta Isn't it exciting!

Chiaretta What shall we do?

Perduta Leave it to me. I've got an idea . . . Sisters?

Grimaldo Still here, little cherub? If you don't go to your beds, Sister Miserere will begin to get cross with you!

Pazzo OK, I give up!

Perduta Do you know what happened last week, Sisters?

Grimaldo No little *putto*, tell us.

Perduta Two men got in here. Actually into the convent! Terribly not allowed!

Grimaldo Never!

Pazzo I can't imagine it!

Grimaldo Surely not!

Perduta It was thrillingly exciting!

Grimaldo It must have been, little Madonna.

Perduta Do you know what happened?

Pazzo Tell us, little daisy chain.

Perduta They got torn to pieces. Both of them. The bits were thrown into the canal.

The two men laugh uproariously, but not altogether heartily

No, really, I'm serious! Just up that corridor, there are a thousand girls of all ages. They've only just got off to sleep. They're really tough girls, they are, from the streets of Venice, all ages, up to nineteen.

Grimaldo Really, little treasure? And what did they do?

Perduta They get very angry, those girls do, if the convent is desecrated. They fell on those two poor fellows like a pack of wolves. Didn't they, girls?

Margarita You couldn't help feeling sorry for them.

Giulietta They were simply overwhelmed!

Fortunata They were very brave and strong. But they didn't have a chance.

Chiaretta Not against a thousand girls in a raging fury!

Grimaldo And what did you say happened?

Pazzo Tore them to pieces?

Perduta It was terrible. We little ones had to clear up all the blood. Then some of the brawny nuns, the tough ones with the big muscles, put all the bits in a basket and threw them into the canal. The Doge's secret police came here a week later, looking for them. Apparently they were criminals on the run. But they didn't find a thing.

Margarita Not one shred of flesh!

Giulietta Not a chip of bone!

Chiaretta Not a fingernail!

Fortunata Not a hair!

Margarita They just disappeared.

Giulietta From the face of the earth.

Fortunata For ever and ever.

Chiaretta Amen.

Perduta They got caught, of course. If they'd managed to slip out without being suspected . . .

Pazzo Yes . . . Sister Benedicta?

Grimaldo Yes Sister . . . er . . . um . . .?

Pazzo Never mind, forget it, let's get out of here!

Grimaldo What about the music?

Pazzo To Hell with the music! Let's get to the main gate!

Grimaldo I can't remember which way!

Pazzo Just run, you fool! Run!

They run off in utter disarray

Perduta And next time you want to be a nun, make sure your boots aren't showing!

Margarita And have a better shave!

The girls laugh, as the scene changes to the interior of the Pietà at night, The setting is as before, with Vivaldi's area DL and the central area representing the hall

The Governor comes in, followed by Vandini. They are both cloaked and masked for the carnival

Governor Vandini!

Vandini Yes, signore?

Governor What's going on?

Vandini I don't know, signore.

Governor I had a message from Vivaldi to meet him here at once.

Vandini So did I, signore.

Governor At this time of night, in the middle of the Carnival? What does he think he's doing? I was having a wonderful time. Weren't you?

Vandini Transports of joy, signore, indeed . . .

Vivaldi enters briskly, wearing no trace of a Carnival costume

Governor Ah, here he is. Maestro Vivaldi, what do you mean by this peremptory summons, why have you called us here?

Vivaldi Because I am too busy to come to you. I've a motet and two concertos to finish by tomorrow midday.

Governor But that's nothing to do with me, why did you —

Vivaldi To tell you I'm resigning. And so is Vandini, aren't you!

Vandini What? Am I? Well, I mean —

Vivaldi I'm going back to Prague, and Vandini is coming with me. And all the other teachers are resigning too, all coming to Prague!

Governor But you can't do that Maestro, what on earth . . . ?

Vivaldi The organist, Maestra Luciana, the very greatest artist in Venice, quite indispensable. You've sacked her.

Governor We have told her —

Vivaldi You sack her, you sack me, you sack everyone! I can't possibly work without her. She is the most important person here except for me. As soon as I have finished the concerto, I will pack my bags.

Governor We have to save money, Maestro, she has to go.

Vivaldi Then save money on me too, and Vandini, and first of all, sack yourself!

Governor Maestro Don Antonio —

Vivaldi She goes, I go, and I take all my music with me. If I play my Seasons Concertos, every day of the week, every day of the week that church will be full! Without me, it will be empty! Nobody there, no money at all. The Pietà slowly sinks into the canal, and all the Governors sink with it. And we make a fortune in Prague, don't we Vandini!

Vandini Do we? Oh, yes, er, we do, certainly!

Vivaldi marches off. Vandini following

Governor Well, I suppose, in that case . . . if you really feel . . .

They both march back

Vivaldi Good, the matter is settled. Maestra Luciana teaches organ here, as long as *she* wishes to.

Governor Of course, I shall have to consult —

Vivaldi No consulting. Or I catch the next boat.

Governor Very well, since she is so important to your plans . . .

Vivaldi She is crucial! That's all, signore. You can go back to your masked ball. I've finished with you.

Governor *(furiously)* I . . . I . . .

Vivaldi Yes?

Governor Good-morning, Maestro!

Vivaldi Good-morning, signore!

The Governor stamps out

Vandini You weren't really going to Prague?

Vivaldi No, of course not.

Vandini I couldn't possibly. No-one knows me there.

Vivaldi Neither could I. I'm utterly broke, and there's no money in Prague. All the money is in Venice!

Vandini You took a great risk, Maestro. Supposing he had accepted your resignation?

Vivaldi Then all three of us would have been out of a job. I can't stand the woman, but she is a musician. These people are our servants, Vandini. Like melons, we slit them open, suck out all the juice we want, then throw away the rind. The man has the mind of a banker.

Vandini He is a banker.

Anna-Maria enters, and stands at a distance. They do not see her. She has changed back into her Pietà habit

Vivaldi Of course he is, what else would he be! We need them, old friend, we can't work without their cash. But we must make sure they know their places!

Vandini Well, good-night, Don Antonio. Please don't do that to me again. I don't think my nerves could stand it. You are famous throughout Europe, and will get what you want. But I am not, and must hang on to what I have.

Vivaldi For a time, old friend, only for a time: in both our cases. So we must make the most of it!

Vandini exits

Anna-Maria emerges as Vivaldi goes into his area L, getting ready to work

Anna-Maria Maestro Vivaldi . . . Can I speak to you for a moment?

Vivaldi Maestr'Anna! What are you doing here at this time of night? You should be either in your bed, or out in a gondola somewhere with your lover.

Anna-Maria I have no lover, Maestro . . . and I am in despair. (*She is in tears*)

Vivaldi Now . . . despair? Artists never despair. It stops them from working.

Anna-Maria I can't work anymore. I am too old! I have to leave!

Vivaldi But you are getting married. An English nobleman. What could be better?

Anna-Maria No. I'm not.

Vivaldi No?

Anna-Maria (*almost hysterical*) No Maestro! No, No, No!

Vivaldi Don't shout at me, child. I am too old and too ill to endure anyone's shouting but my own. So. It is to be the nunnery.

Anna-Maria No, it isn't!

Vivaldi Then what?

Anna-Maria I have to be a musician. I have to be!

Vivaldi But you cannot be. You know that.

Anna-Maria I can, I can sing. Women can sing . . .

Vivaldi My child . . .

Anna-Maria I have to sing! I beg you, Maestro, let me sing! You are presenting an opera season in Venice this summer, let me sing for you . . .

Vivaldi You are a violinist, a great one . . .

Anna-Maria But I can't do that, there are no women players, not in opera houses, not in court orchestras! I am a good singer, and I will get better. I beg you, let me sing for you. I will never touch my violin again, I will throw it in the canal if you let me sing for you!

Vivaldi. Listen child! . . . You know nothing, you have lived your life in a convent, and you have no understanding of the world, or what a singer's life is like, what any artist's life is like! It isn't only making beautiful sounds. It's having the right aristocratic protector, who will guard you with his paid assassins, from other aristocratic gentlemen, and keep you in his palace for his private use when you are not in the Opera House. It means repaying his favours with your own, in whatever way he asks. It means keeping at least two others in the background, unknown to the first, who are just as mad to get you on to their stages and into their beds, so that when the first drops you, as he will, you are not left naked in the street. It's being kidnapped at the stage door because some Cardinal has taken a fancy to you, and Princes of the Church must have their way, even over noblemen sometimes. It means working too hard, and singing too often, bullying composers to write you showy enough arias so that your reputation doesn't slide. It means losing your voice at fifty and your looks at thirty-five, and dying in poverty in a gutter somewhere, starved, ill or murdered. It's spending your whole life thinking of money, power and reputation, and whose property you are this week, just to ensure that when the moment comes, you can open your mouth and practise your art, and do what you were born to do. An artist lives for money, fame, reputation and power, because without those things he cannot practise his art, and that is all that matters to him, more than house, home, pleasure,

more even than life. I am a composing machine, that's all. I became a
priest, because it was the only way a poor boy could get an education,
but I never say Mass, and have not done for twenty years, because I have
no time for anything but music. I have a mania for it, a consuming power
that I can't control. I compose like a madman, like a wheatfield swept by
the wind of God, or a forest on fire, I can do nothing else. Sometimes it
is good, sometimes less good, sometimes so bad it makes me weep for
having written it, but I can't stop the fire burning, and everything in my
life, everything, comes second to that flame. You can't do that. You can't
live like that. All opera singers are monsters, because they have to be
if they are to practise their art to the best of their ability. You are not a
monster. Go to a convent and live in peace.

Anna-Maria I can't.

Vivaldi You must. I can't give you a place in my company. You have never
sung in opera.

Anna-Maria I can't, Maestro. I am on fire too. It burns in my heart just as
you describe it in yours.

Vivaldi No. It's not possible.

Anna-Maria It must be. I can't live any other way.

Vivaldi I can't do it.

Anna-Maria How can I stay alive, Maestro, without music? What is there
left, but the canal!

A pause

Vivaldi You would do that?

Anna-Maria What else can I do? If I can't make music, there is nothing to
live for.

A pause

Vivaldi Very well. I will write you a small part in my new opera. And we
shall see what you can do. How will you live till the Summer?

Anna-Maria I have saved a little from my teaching. I shall take a room.

Vivaldi I can pay you nothing.

Anna-Maria No, you must pay me what you pay the other singers playing
their first parts.

Vivaldi What? How dare you haggle with me about cash!

Anna-Maria If I am a professional, I am worth my pay. Next season I shall
ask you for more.

Vivaldi Good God! Opera singers are the bane of my life! And here I am
making another rod for my own back!

Anna-Maria There is no art without money, Maestro, you said so yourself.

Vivaldi Very well, we shall haggle about that when the time comes. What
is the concert tomorrow?

Anna-Maria In the Golden House, on the Grand Canal.

Vivaldi And you're playing a violin concerto?

Anna-Maria Yes, Maestro.

Vivaldi Prudenza can play it. You will sing my motet *In Furore*. Every day you will sing, the most difficult music I can find for you . . .

Anna-Maria Thank you, Maestro, thank you. You have saved my life!

Vivaldi No child, I have saved the art in you, that's all, because I begin to think it is real. There is nothing in my life more important than that. Not success, not fame, not even money. They are all servants. But this is the master of us all. Make sure you serve it too.

Anna-Maria Yes Maestro, I will!

The lights change, the stage fills with the full orchestra and chorus of the Pietà, preparing to give a concert

Vandini comes in and addresses the orchestra

Vivaldi and Anna-Maria have not left the stage

Vandini My children . . . daughters of the Muse . . . the Contessas and Contes, the Grand Dukes and Duchesses, have all eaten themselves almost to extinction, and are ready for the concert. Play well my daughters, be worthy. Take your places, and make music!

With a great feeling of controlled excitement, the orchestra goes off stage to play

Vandini and Vivaldi are left alone onstage

Vivaldi Not playing today, Maestro Vandini? Not sharing in all that energy, all that sadness, all that joy?

Vandini No, Maestro. Nor you.

Vivaldi We're getting old and lazy, Vandini. The public expects to see us there, sawing away at the first desk. But tonight I prefer to listen. And most of these girls are as good as we are! Or nearly as good.

Vandini As good as I am, Maestro. Not as good as you.

The opening ritornello of "In Furore" begins off stage

Ah . . . they've begun. Shall we go in?

Vivaldi No, just a moment.

They listen together, rapt. At the end of the ritornello Anna-Maria's voice is heard, fiery, dramatic, singing the solo part. Vivaldi nods

The child's good. She is one of us.

Vandini She is an artist, to the very centre of her soul.

Vivaldi God help her.

Vandini Shall we go in and listen? She's worth listening to.

Vivaldi Yes. Let's go in and listen.

The two musicians go off stage together

The music swells till it fills the theatre with the triumph of its art

CURTAIN

FURNITURE AND PROPERTY LIST

ACT I

The vestry
On stage: Lockers. *By them*: instrument cases, pieces of music, dark hooded cloaks

Off stage: Large pile of music manuscripts **(Perduta)**
Instruments, folders of music **(Orchestra)** – see script for individual instruments

Personal: **Anna-Maria, Silvia, Candida, Lucietta, Prudenza, Soprana, Anastazia**: flowers in their hair

A street
On stage: Nil
No props required

The Madre's room
On stage: Table. *On it*: pen, ink
Chairs
Many ledgers
Large crucifix on wall

A street
On stage: Nil
No props required

The Madre's room
On stage: As before, plus:
Lighted lamp, ledger on desk

Bedroom DL
On stage: Bed
Off stage: Lighted lamps **(Prudenza, Pellegrina, Michelotta)**
Box with costumes and masks **(Paulina)**

Bedroom DL
On stage: Bed
Lighted lamp

The Madre's room
On stage: As before
Off stage: Ledger, locket, shawl, note **(Sister Annunciata)**

Reception room
On stage: Wall with two windows with grilles and curtain on one side
Chairs, stools

	Punch and Judy booth with puppets
	Recorder for **Boy**
	3 puppets for **Puppet Boy**
	Tray with ribbons and lace for **Pedlar Girl**
Off stage:	Basket with bread rolls (**Sister Teresa**)
Personal:	**Bodger**: 5 pennies in pocket

An ante room
On stage:	Chairs
Off stage:	Instruments (**Orchestra**)
	Folders of music (**Perduta**)
Personal:	**Vivaldi**: walking-stick (required throughout)

ACT II

The Madre's room
On stage:	As before
Off stage:	Small bundle of shawl, locket (**Perduta**)

A street
On stage:	Nil
Off stage:	Barrow containing paintings covered by cloth (**Pazzo**)
Personal:	**Milord**: mask
	Bodger: mask
	Pazzo: mask, bottle of wine and glass under costume
	Grimaldo: mask

Interior of the Pietà
On stage:	Table with pen and ink, chair DL
	Chair, illuminated sheet or shadow wall DR
Off stage:	Instruments (**Orchestra**)
	Bundle of manuscript music (**Vivaldi**)

A square
On stage:	Café tables. *On them*: glasses
	Chairs
Off stage:	Coloured lanterns on long poles (**Revellers**)
	Flasks and jugs of wine (**Waiters**)
	Pipe and tabor (**Street Performers**)
	Lamps (**Revellers**)
Personal:	**Revellers**: masks
	Young Man: mask
	Milord: mask as before
	Bodger: red devil mask
	Candida: white mask
	Mr Punch: mask
	Prudenza: red devil mask
	Pellegrina, Paulina, Michelotta: masks

The Madre's room
On stage: As before

The square
On stage: As before
Off stage: Lighted lantern (**Reveller**)
                       Flask of wine (**Bodger**)
Personal: **Anna-maria:** Columbine mask
                       Silvia: gold mask

The library
On stage: Old books of music
                       Loose MS sheets
                       Table. *On it*: lighted lamp
                       Chairs

Interior of the Pietà
On stage: As before
Personal: **Governor:** mask
                       Vandini: mask

An ante room
Off stage: Instruments (**Orchestra**)

LIGHTING PLOT

Practical fittings required: lamps
Various simple interior and exterior settings

ACT I

To open: Lighting on vestry

Printed and bound by
The Cromwell Press Limited,
Broughton Gifford, Melksham,
Wiltshire

ACT II

To open: Lighting on Madre's room

Cue 12   **Sister Annunciata** follows **Contessa** out;
           Madre stands still   (Page 44)
           Cross-fade to street

Cue 13   **Milord** and **Bodger** go off, wheeling barrow   (Page 47)
           Cross-fade to interior of Pietà; light on sheet DR

Cue 14   As **Anna-Maria** and **Silvia** go off   (Page 54)
           *Cross-fade to square – early evening; light streaming
           out through open windows and doors*

Cue 15   **Bodger**: ". . . a chance of kissing her."   (Page 55)
           Fireworks

Cue 16   **Young Man** slides silently into darkness   (Page 60)
           Cross-fade to Madre's room – early evening

Cue 17   **Madre**: "What other way is there?"   (Page 62)
           Cross-fade to square – night

Cue 18   **Bodger** and **Milord** go off together   (Page 68)
           Cross-fade to library – night, lamp lit

Cue 19   The girls laugh   (Page 71)
           Cross-fade to interior of the Pietà – night

Cue 20   **Anna-Maria**:"Yes, Maestro, I will!"   (Page 75)
           Change to bright interior lighting

EFFECTS PLOT
ACT I

Cue 1 Before CURTAIN rises   (Page 1)
First movement of Vivaldi's concerto "La Tempesta di Mare" Op. 8 No. 5

Cue 2 As CURTAIN rises   (Page 1)
Third movement of above, off – continue

Cue 3 **Luciana**: ". . . lives for ever."   (Page 3)
Concerto comes to an end; rustling of feet, movement of many people, restrained talk – fade as orchestra enter

Cue 4 As **Madre** enters her room   (Page 15)
Instrumental and vocal practice and rehearsal, off – cut as door is closed

Cue 5 As **Governor** enters   (Page 15)
Rehearsal sounds, off

Cue 6 **Contessa** shuts door   (Page 18)
Cut rehearsal sounds

Cue 7 **Madre**: "Leave the things with me."   (Page 29)
Bell begins to ring

Cue 8 Lights fade on groups R, L and C   (Page 30)
Fade bell

Cue 9 As Lights come up on ante room   (Page 35)
Formal minuet plays, off

Cue 10 **Silvia**: " . . . petals at your wedding."   (Page 35)
Minuet ends, low level of talk from guests, off

Cue 11 Girls file into Grand Salon   (Page 36)
Some applause, continue low level of talk

Cue 12 **Vivaldi**: " . . . must pay for his pleasures."   (Page 38)
"Spring" from "The Four Seasons"

Cue 13 **Luciana** slowly sits on chair   (Page 39)
Increase music

ACT II

Cue 14	**Perduta:** "Come on." *Sounds of rehearsal off – continue*	(Page 49)
Cue 15	**Lucietta** and **Soprana** join Silvia behind lighted sheet *Movement of a cello sonata by Vivaldi*	(Page 51)
Cue 16	**Candida** sweeps out *Cello music stops*	(Page 51)
Cue 17	**Silvia** goes behind the sheet *Cello music continues*	(Page 53)
Cue 18	**Anna-Maria** goes C and looks round *Cello sonata finishes*	(Page 54)
Cue 19	**Anna-Maria** and **Silvia** go off *Huge burst of joyful music, then continuous sound of music, from street, from concerts and ball, off*	(Page 54)
Cue 20	**Bodger:** " . . . a chance of kissing her." *Fireworks*	(Page 55)
Cue 21	As scene changes to Madre's room *Fade music and carnival sounds*	(Page 60)
Cue 22	**Madre:** "What other way is there?" *Melancholy music*	(Page 62)
Cue 23	**Bodger** and **Milord** go off together *Fade music*	(Page 68)
Cue 24	**Vandini:** "Not as good as you." *Opening ritornello of "In Furore" begins, off*	(Page 75)
Cue 25	At end of ritornello **Anna-Maria's** *voice sings, off*	(Page 75)
Cue 26	**Vivaldi** and **Vandini** go off together *Music swells*	(Page 75)